Specials!

Resistant materials

Neil Triggs

Acknowledgements

Thank you to the team at Folens for their support during the writing and editing of this book, particularly Nina Randall; the Design and Technology Association's Special Needs Advisory Group for their suggestions and advice and the series editor, Louise T. Davies.

United Kingdom: Folens Publishers, Apex Business Centre, Boscombe Road, Dunstable, LU5 4RL.

Email: folens@folens.com

Ireland: Folens Publishers, Greenhills Road, Tallaght, Dublin 24.

Email: info@folens.ie

Poland: JUKA, ul. Renesansowa 38, Warsaw 01-905

Commissioning Editor: Nina Randall Editor: Daniel Bottom Layout artist: Book Matrix

Illustrations: Julian Baker of JB Illustrations pp3, 7, 8, 9, 10, 12 (kitchen sink, cast iron vice, drinks can, nut and bolt, jewellery display, hosepipe, model kit, cable ties, guttering, syringe and protective packaging), 14 (jewellery display, model kit and syringe), 15 (plastic toy, plastic food box, saucepan, iron I beam, gear wheel and copper pipe), 16 (plywood, drinks can, oak, MDF, nut and bolt and cable ties), 23 (helmet, honeycomb, sea shell, spider's web, skeleton, cave, food tin, steel arch bridge and climbing frame), 24, 25, 29, 30, 31, 32, 35, 36, 37, 38, 39, 41, 42 (workbench, desk, bicycle frame and suitcase), 43 (wax, spray paint, polishing wheel, wood stain, paint, varnish, acrylic vase, children's furniture, dining table, staircase and child's toy), 44, 45, 47, 48, 50, 51 (acrylic vase, Müller corner yoghurt, candlestick holder, acrylic sign/photo holder, vacuum former, CAD/CAM machine, blow moulding machine, simple jig, aluminium sand casting machine), 53, 57, 59, 60, 61; Steph Dix of GCI p12 (electrical wire); Celia Hart p15 (telephone and aeroplane); Annabel Spenceley p42 (picture frame); Peter Wilkes of SGA pp12 (plastic bottle and mobile phone), 14 (mobile phone), 16 (water bottle), 23 (bicycle), 43 (bicycle), 51 (drinks bottle).

Cover design: Holbrook Design Cover image: Alfred Pasieka / Science Photo Library

First published 2007 by Folens Limited.

British Library Cataloguing in Publication Data. A catalogue record for this publication is available from the British Library.

ISBN 978 1 85008 229 3

Contents

Introduction

Specials! D&T is divided into ten units. The activities in Specials! are planned for students with a reading comprehension age of 7 to 9 years and working at levels 1 to 3. Some student pages are more challenging than others and you will need to select accordingly. In most cases, a unit has one or more photocopiable resource sheets and several activity sheets. This allows the teacher to work in different ways. For example, the unit could be taught as a lesson with students in groups of varying sizes. Alternatively, a single resource sheet and its related activity sheets could be used as a support material. The Teacher's pages give guidance and are laid out as follows:

Objectives
These are the main skills or knowledge to be learned.

Prior knowledge
This refers to the recommended skills or knowledge required by the students to begin the tasks. If this is not the case then students may need further support as they begin the activities.

QCA and NC links, Scottish attainment targets, Northern Ireland and Welsh links
All units link to the QCA scheme of work, the NC for Design and Technology at Key Stage 3 and Scottish attainment targets. Where relevant, there are also links to the programmes in Northern Ireland and Wales and the Key Stage 3 Framework of Objectives for D&T. For updated curriculum links, please go to www.folens.com.

Background
This gives additional information for the teacher, about this unit.

Starter activity
Since the units can be taught as a lesson, a warm-up activity focusing on an aspect of the unit, is suggested.

Resource and activity sheets
The resource sheet, which is often visual, but may also be written, usually includes no tasks and can be used as stimulus for discussion. Related tasks are provided on activity sheets. Where necessary, key words are included on the student pages. Other key words are included within the Teacher's notes. These can be introduced to students at the teacher's discretion and depending on the students' ability.

Plenary
The teacher can use the suggestions here to recap on the main points covered or to reinforce a particular idea.

Assessment sheet
At the end of each unit, students can use the assessment sheet to assess their own progress. Students can subsequently set targets to achieve according to their performance.

Look out for other titles in the Design and Technology series, which include:

- Designing and making
- Food
- Systems and control
- Textiles

Teacher's notes

Materials (1)

Objectives

- To gain knowledge and understanding of different types of timber and their properties
- To be able to match suitable timbers to common uses
- To recognise how the properties of a material suit particular products

Prior knowledge

To achieve these objectives, students should have some basic knowledge of different types of trees and be able to recognise the difference between natural and manufactured timber.

QCA links

Unit 7a (ii) Understanding materials – resistant materials.

NC links

4) Knowledge and understanding of materials and components: (c).

Northern Ireland PoS

Knowledge and understanding – manufacturing materials.

Scottish attainment targets

Environmental Studies – Technology
Strand – Resources and how they are managed
Levels C and D

Welsh PoS

Materials: 1).

Background

This unit will focus on the origins of different types of timber, concentrating on the soft and hardwood of coniferous and deciduous trees. It also focuses on the production, uses and properties of both manufactured boards and timber. Through this unit, students should gain the knowledge and understanding they need to enable them to select suitable timber depending on the intended use and design of a product.

Starter activity

Ask students to describe the difference between soft and hardwood trees that they may have seen in parks and the countryside. It should be possible to broaden the discussion into the differences between manufactured and natural timber.

Resource and activity sheets

Discuss 'Types of timber' with the students, linking the materials to common products that they may find in the workshop or classroom and at home. Most students should understand the concepts of hardwood and softwood, and natural and manufactured timbers. They may struggle to read the different names of timbers used on the resource sheet and activity sheets. If necessary, read through these with students and, where possible, show examples of the timbers.

For the activity sheet 'Properties of materials' you may prefer the students to work in pairs so that they can discuss the pictures and names and try to group them together. They should then answer the questions.

To introduce 'Properties of timber', refer the students to the resource sheet 'Types of timber' again and also the properties of the timbers that were discussed earlier. You may wish to discuss key words such as durable, flexible, grain, ease of use and cost.

'Matching materials to products (1)' and '(2)' ask students to match the products to the different types of timber by identifying the properties that are needed.

Plenary

Recap the main focus of the lesson by asking the students to name some timber samples that you have provided for them – identifying softwood, hardwood and manufactured timbers – and try to elicit the properties of each that they have learned. If possible, have a few examples of wooden products on the table that students can look at and discuss.

Types of timber

Natural timber

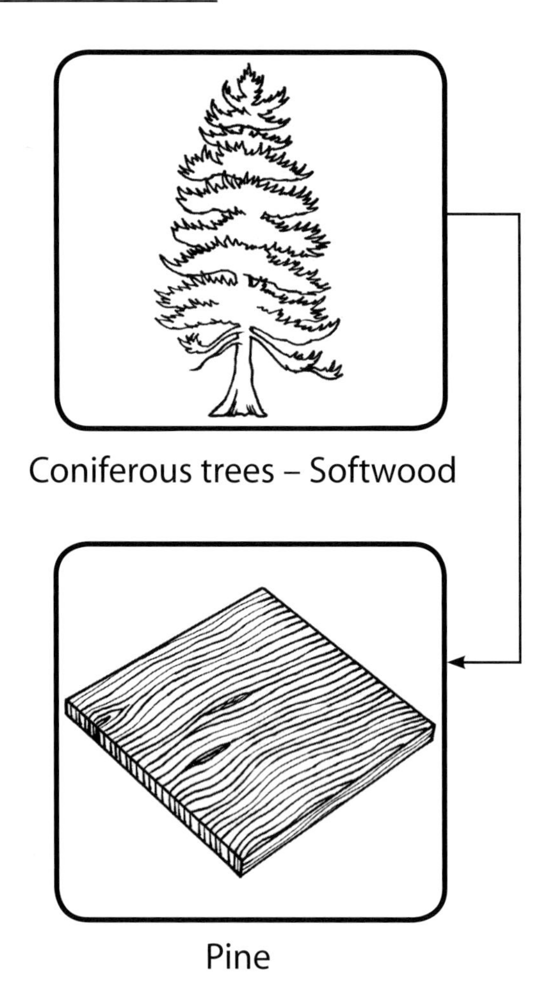

Coniferous trees – Softwood

Pine

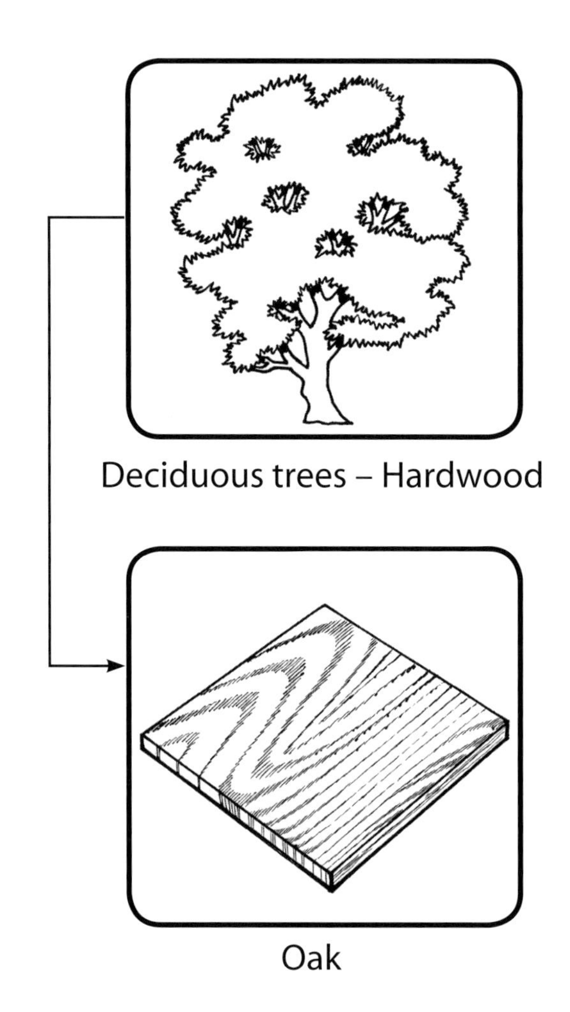

Deciduous trees – Hardwood

Oak

Manufactured timber

Plywood

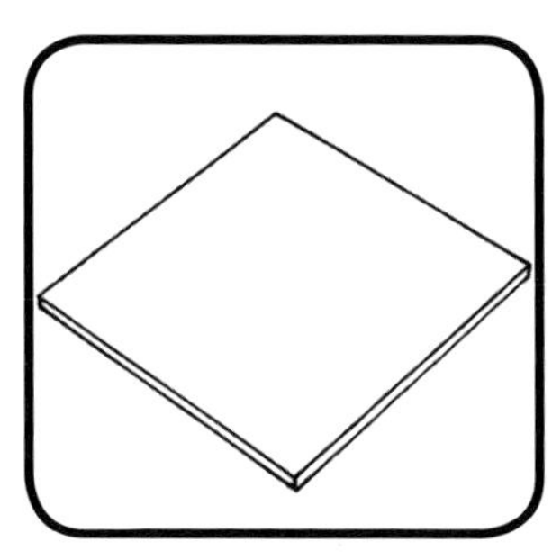

Medium Density Fibreboard (MDF)

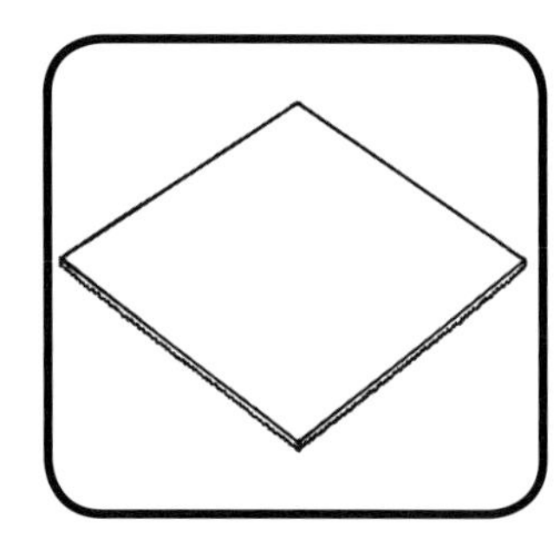

Hardboard

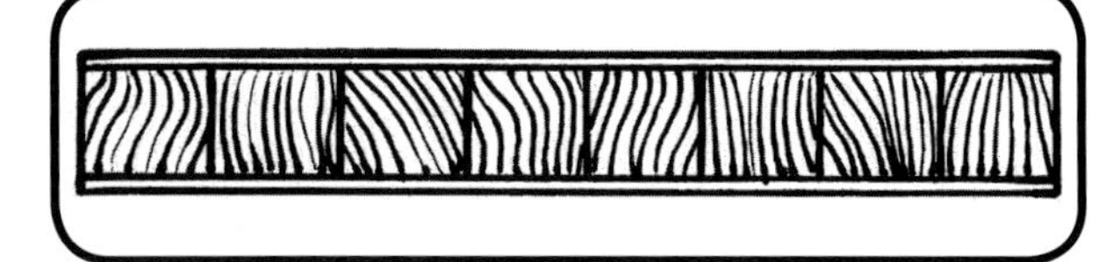

Blockboard

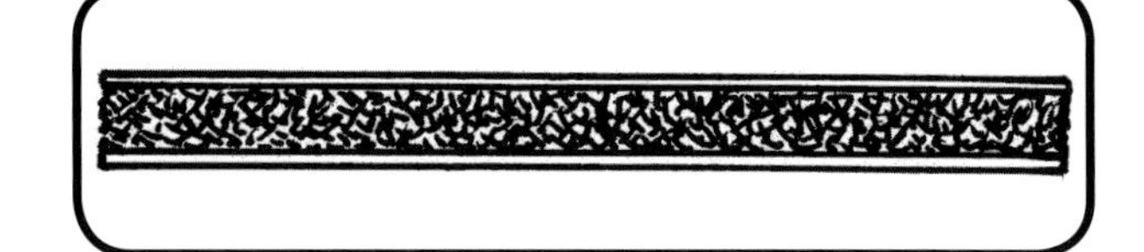

Chipboard

Properties of materials

☞ Look at the resource sheet 'Types of timber' and complete the tasks below.

Describe a **deciduous** tree and name as many examples as you can.

Describe a **coniferous tree** and name as many examples as you can.

Describe how **plywood** is produced and what makes it strong.

Describe how **Medium Density Fibreboard (MDF)** is made.

Properties of timber

☞ Complete the table below using the examples of timber that your teacher has provided you with. Name each material and draw or glue a sample in the column labelled 'Material'.

Material	Properties

Matching materials to products (1)

☞ Use the word banks below to complete the tables on 'Matching materials to products (1)' and '(2)'. Identify the type of timber used for each product and the properties that make the material suitable.

Materials

Mahogany Oak Beech Teak Balsa Pine Red Deal Red Ceder Plywood Medium Density Fibreboard Blockboard

Properties

durable stable strong light weather resistant suitable for outdoor use flexible decorative expensive cheap

Product	Material	Properties
Chair		
Fruit bowl		
Flat-packed desk		
Mallet		

Matching materials to products (2)

Product	Material	Properties
Garden table		
Spoon		
Desk		
Jewellery box		
Roof structure		

Teacher's notes

Materials (2)

Objectives

- To be able to classify materials according to their properties' uses and type
- To develop the ability to gain information on materials from a variety of sources
- To select materials according to the needs of the product

Prior knowledge

To achieve these objectives and complete the tasks in this unit satisfactorily, students should first complete 'Materials (1)'.

QCA links

Unit 7a (ii) Understanding materials – resistant materials.

NC links

4) Knowledge and understanding of materials and components: (b).

Northern Ireland PoS

Knowledge and understanding – manufacturing materials.

Scottish attainment targets

Environmental Studies – Technology
Strand – Resources and how they are managed
Level D
Strand – Needs and how they are met
Level D

Welsh PoS

Materials: 1) and Designing skills: 2).

Background

This unit will build upon the knowledge students have gained through the unit 'Materials (1)' and extend it by focusing on a range of other materials with which they are likely to come into contact with in Design and Technology. Once students have completed this unit, they should feel confident in selecting an appropriate material, based on the type of product and the location where it is likely to be used.

Starter activity

Have a range of products made from different materials set out on the desks. Try to select a few from 'Common metals and plastics' and ask the students, in small groups, to try to name the materials that the products are made from. While taking feedback, introduce the different categories of metals (ferrous and non-ferrous) and plastics (thermoplastic and thermosetting). Encourage the groups to come up with a definition for these categories and then agree a definition with the whole class.

Resource and activity sheets

Introduce 'Common metals and plastics' and discuss the products on the resource sheet that you have not used in the starter. Reinforce the categories discussed and question students on what other products could be made from the range of the materials listed, for example, cutlery from stainless steel.

Use 'Properties of metals' and 'Properties of plastics' to see if students, in pairs, can link the properties of these materials to the products on the resource sheet. They should cut out the products from 'Common metals and plastics' and glue them into a table in their workbooks. They should also suggest other products that could be produced from the same material.

'Matching products to materials' can then be used to reinforce the knowledge that students have gained by asking them to think of the material that each product is likely to be made from and to suggest the properties of that material that make it suitable. At this stage, encourage the students to first select the material on their own without referring to the other sheets, before checking with their partner if they have selected the correct material and discussing the properties that the material should have to be suitable.

Use 'Materials quiz' to see what knowledge the students have retained on the two units of work 'Materials (1)' and '(2)'. Allow up to 15 minutes for the students to complete the test before going through it as a class. Encourage students to make corrections as you go through the possible answers.

Plenary

Through a question and answer session, explore the students' knowledge and understanding of their work on materials so far. Try and draw out in-depth responses using questions such as, '*Explain why teak might be a suitable material for garden furniture*' and '*Why do you think a kitchen sink is made out of stainless steel?*'

Common metals and plastics

Metals

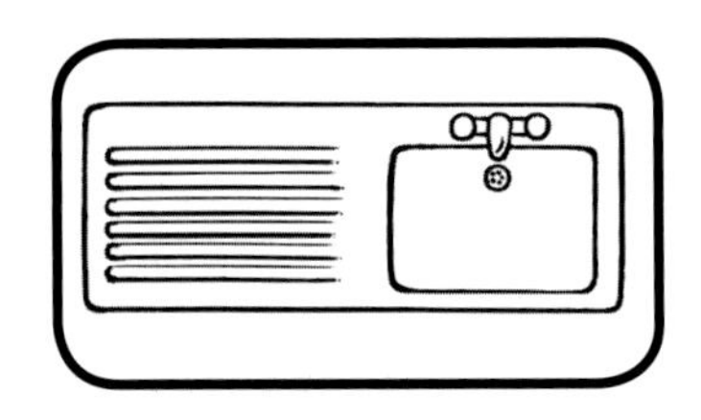
Kitchen sink – Stainless steel

Drinks can – Aluminium

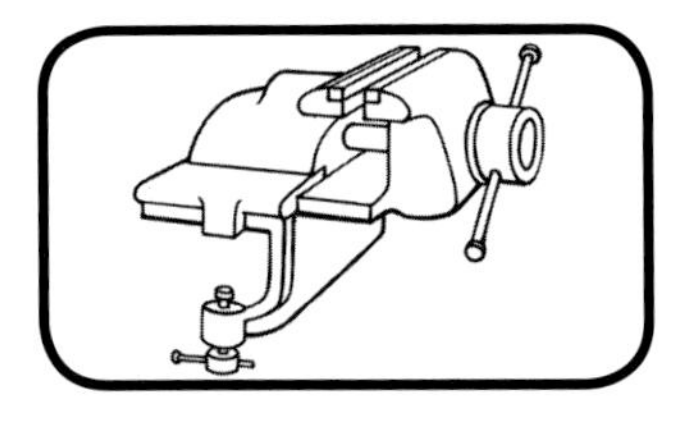
Vice – Cast iron

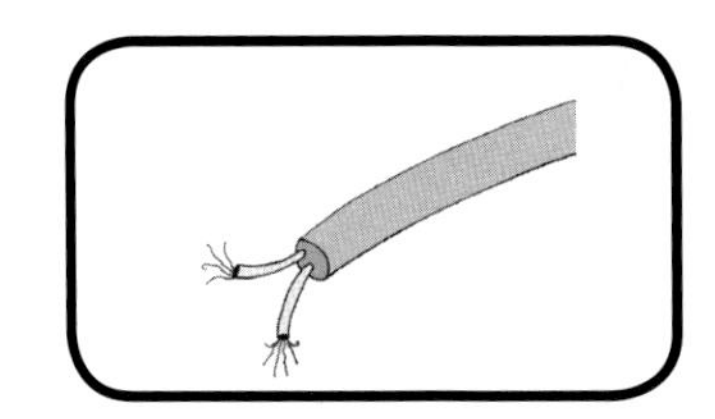
Electrical wire – Copper

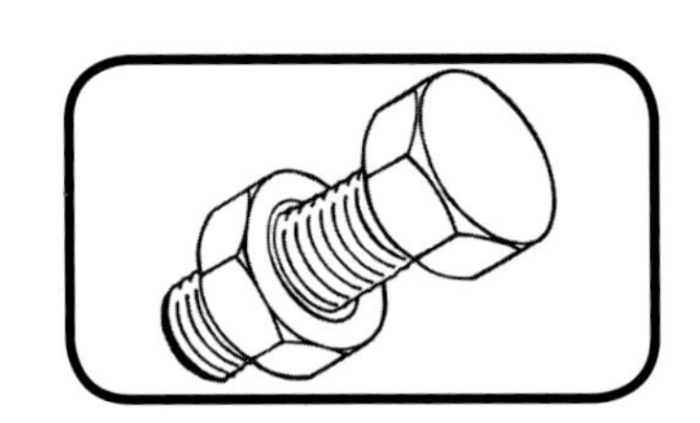
Nut and bolt – Mild steel

Plastics

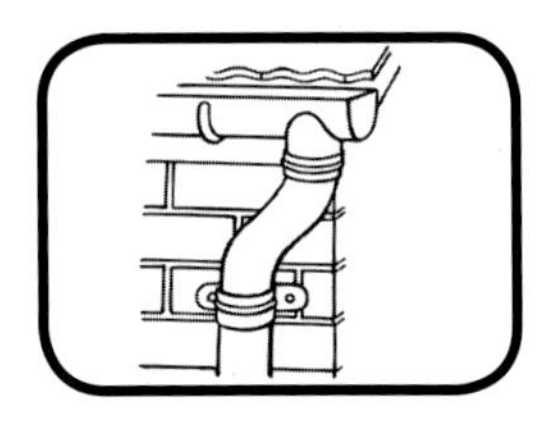
Guttering – Polyvinyl chloride (uPVC)

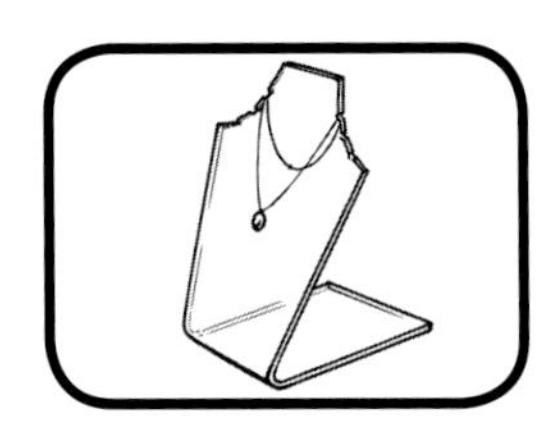
Jewellery display – Acrylic

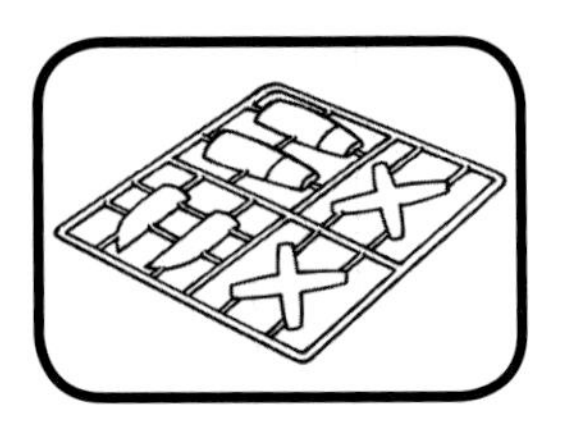
Model kits – Polystyrene

Hosepipe – Plasticised polyvinyl chloride (PVC)

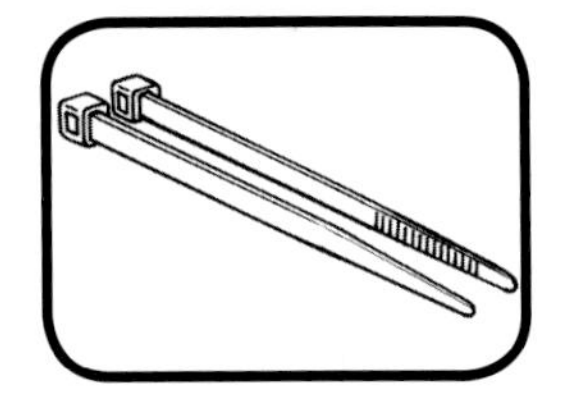
Cable ties – Nylon

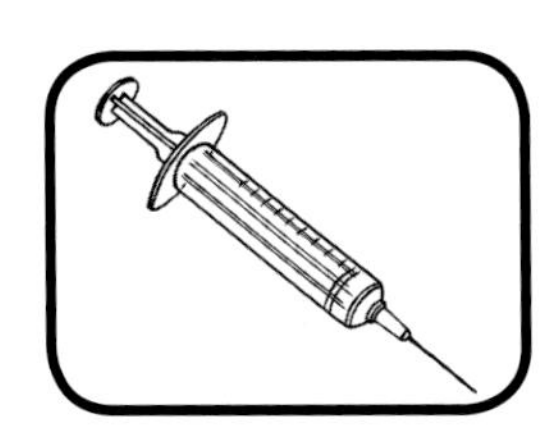
Syringe – Polypropylene

Mobile phones – Acrylonitrile butadiene styrene (ABS)

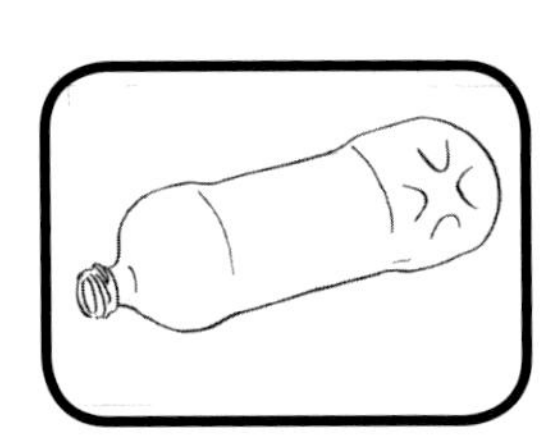
Drinks bottle – Polythene

Properties of metals

☞ Discuss the properties below with a partner. Then cut out the metals from the resource sheet 'Common metals and plastics' and the properties on this sheet. Match them up in your workbook and then list other products that might be made from each material.

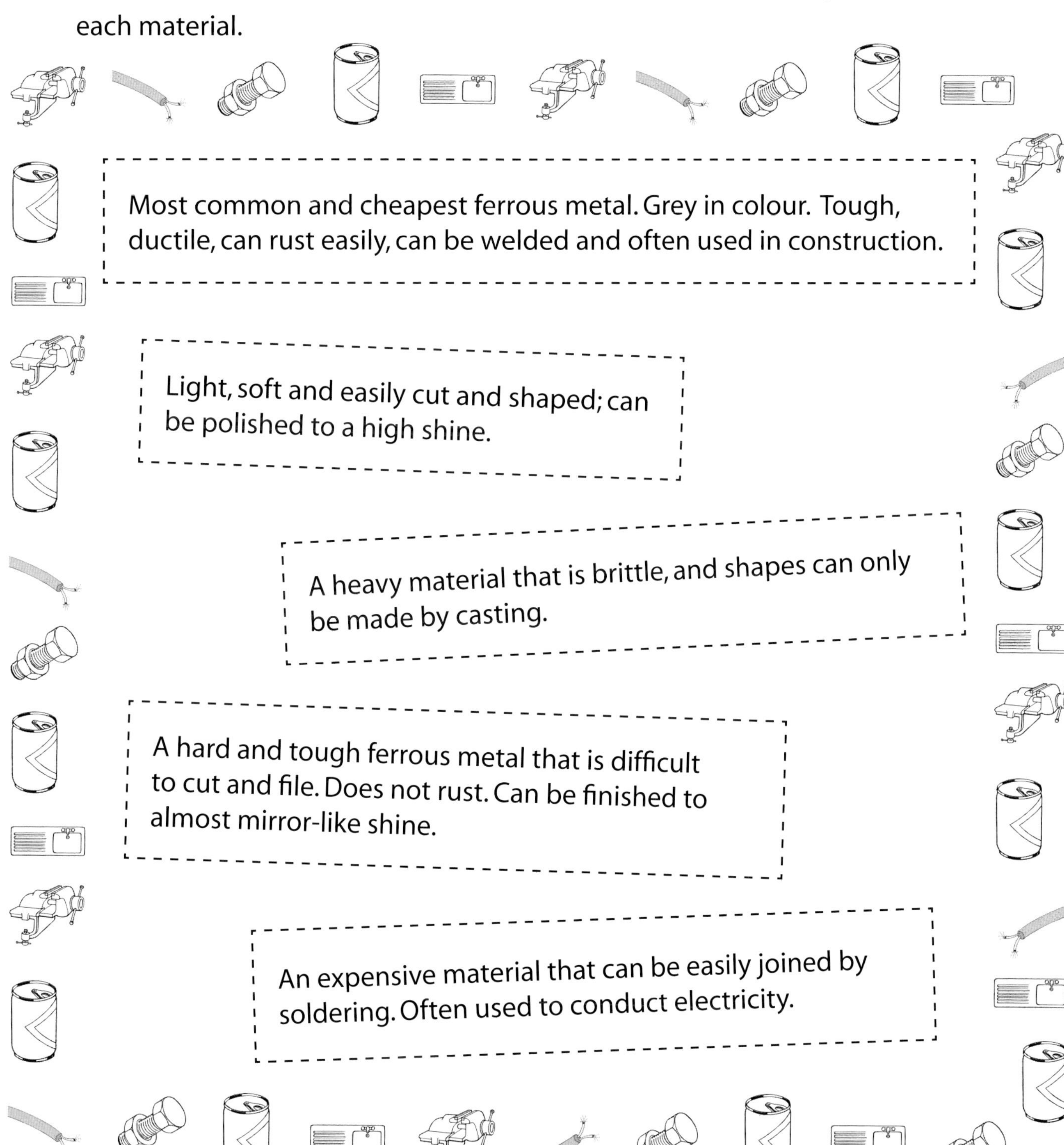

Most common and cheapest ferrous metal. Grey in colour. Tough, ductile, can rust easily, can be welded and often used in construction.

Light, soft and easily cut and shaped; can be polished to a high shine.

A heavy material that is brittle, and shapes can only be made by casting.

A hard and tough ferrous metal that is difficult to cut and file. Does not rust. Can be finished to almost mirror-like shine.

An expensive material that can be easily joined by soldering. Often used to conduct electricity.

☞ See if you can add another metal and its properties.

Properties of plastics

☞ Discuss the properties below with a partner. Then cut out the plastics from the resource sheet 'Common metals and plastics' and the properties on this sheet. Match them up in your workbook and then list other products that might be made from each material. See if you can add another plastic and its properties.

Properties

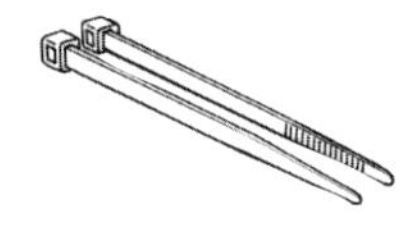

High impact strength, scratch resistant, light and durable. High surface finish.

Tough, common plastic. Good chemical resistance. Flexible electrical insulator, wide range of colours.

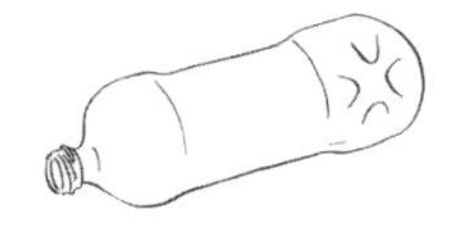

Light, hard, impact-resistant even at low temperatures, can be sterilised, easily joined, welded, good resistance to bending. Can be vacuum formed.

Brittle, low impact strength – safe with food, good water resistance.

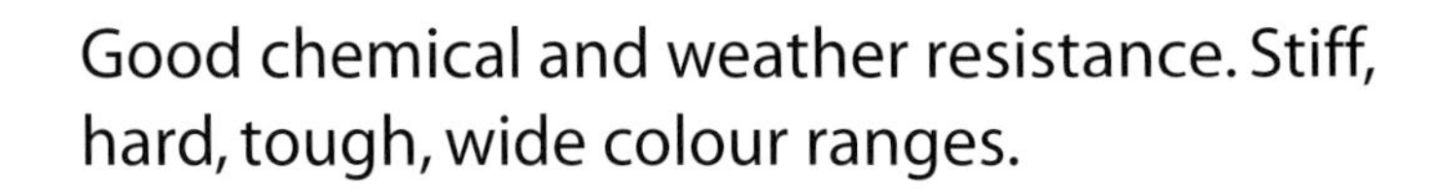

Good chemical and weather resistance. Stiff, hard, tough, wide colour ranges.

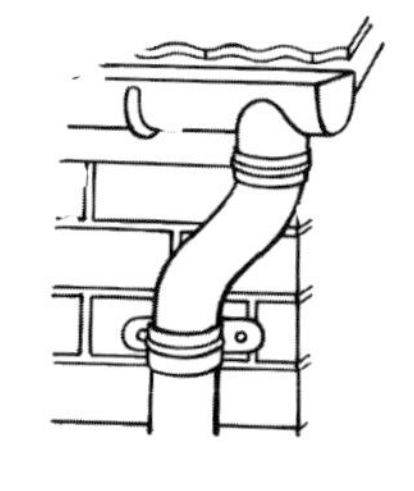

Soft, flexible, good electrical conductor, can be used outdoors.

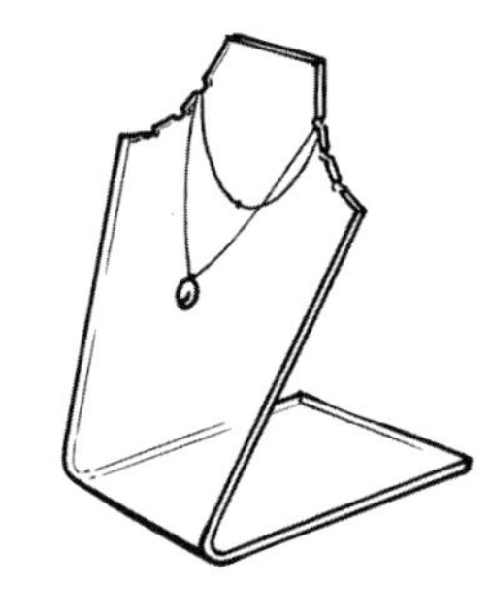

Stiff, hard, can be clear or coloured, can be easily machined, scratches easily – can shatter, polishes well.

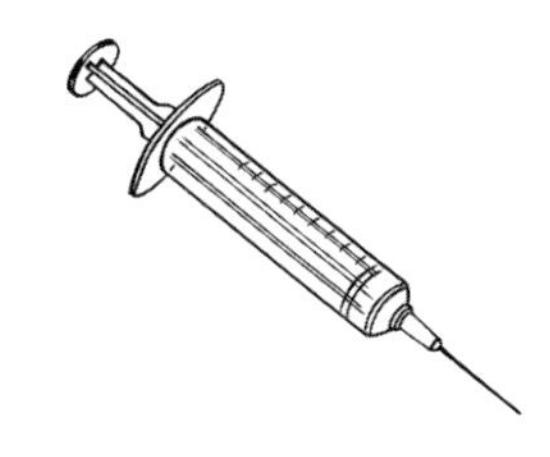

Hard, tough, resistant to wear, low friction – can be used for bearing surfaces, clothing and so on.

Matching products to materials

☞ Choose the most suitable material for the products below and list the properties which make it suitable. You can work in pairs.

Product	Material	Properties
Plastic child's toy		
Plastic food storage box		
Stainless steel saucepan		
Iron I Beam		
Telephone		
Gear wheel		
Copper pipe		
Aeroplane		

Materials quiz

☞ Complete the test below in your workbook.

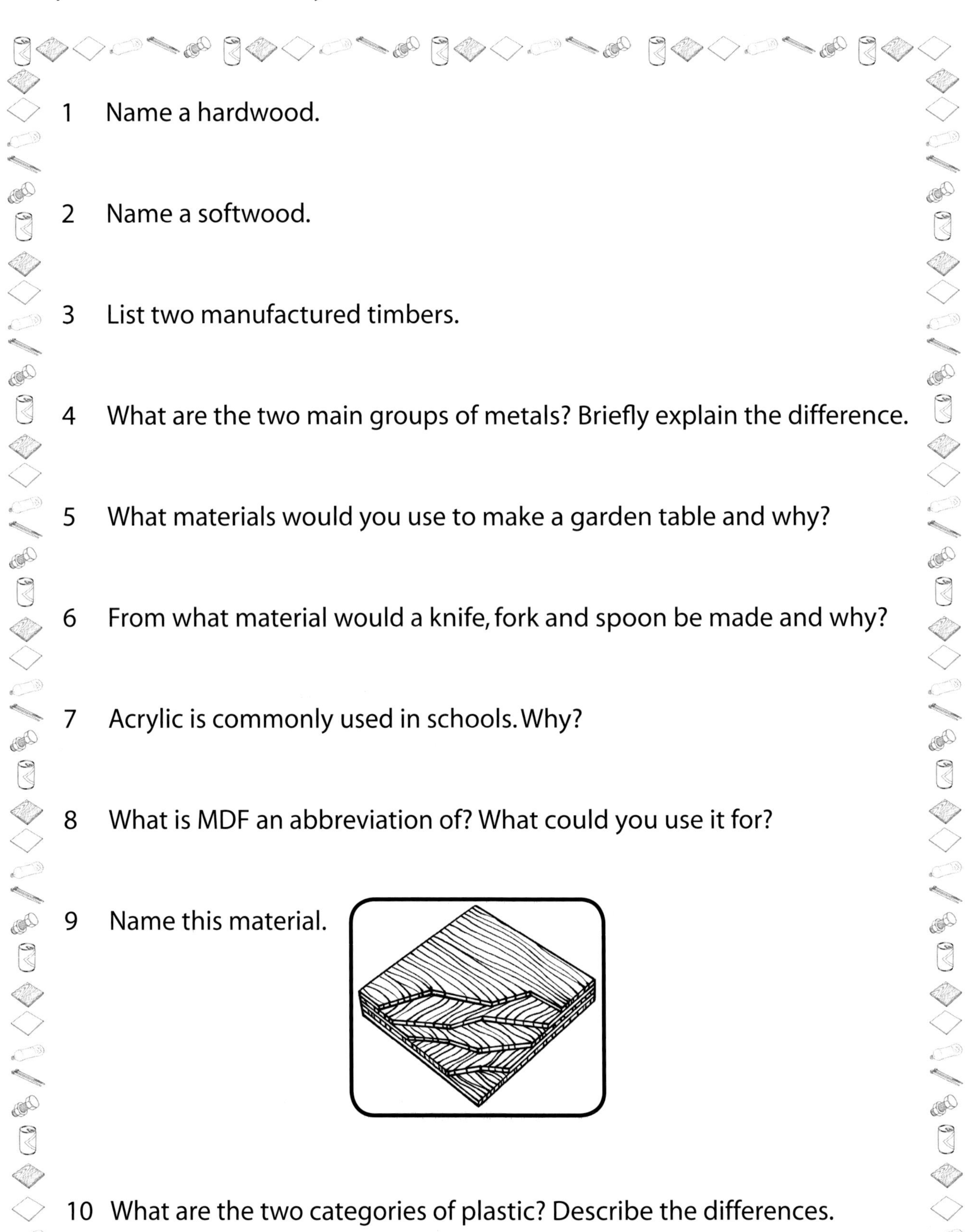

1 Name a hardwood.

2 Name a softwood.

3 List two manufactured timbers.

4 What are the two main groups of metals? Briefly explain the difference.

5 What materials would you use to make a garden table and why?

6 From what material would a knife, fork and spoon be made and why?

7 Acrylic is commonly used in schools. Why?

8 What is MDF an abbreviation of? What could you use it for?

9 Name this material.

10 What are the two categories of plastic? Describe the differences.

Teacher's notes

Designing with resistant materials

Objectives

- To know what a designer needs to think about when designing a product
- To be able to recognise that products are designed to meet particular needs
- To be able to analyse a range of products to determine their suitability for the intended use

Prior knowledge

To achieve these objectives, students should be able to recognise that products are designed with a particular user in mind.

QCA links

Unit 7b (ii) Designing and making for yourself – resistant materials, with reference to Unit 8b (ii) Designing for clients.

NC links

1) Developing, planning and communicating ideas: b).

Northern Ireland PoS

Designing a).

Scottish attainment targets

Environmental studies – Technology
Strand – Processes and how they are applied
Levels D and E
Strand – Needs and how they are met
Level D
Environmental studies – Skills in Technology – designing and making
Strand – Carrying out tasks
Level D

Welsh PoS

Materials: 1) and Designing skills: 1); 3).

Background

This unit will explore the early stages of the design process, encouraging students to carefully consider the needs of the user and what elements must be included in a product's design. Students will look at the people designers usually consider and break this down into the common groupings of ourselves, clients and markets.

Starter activity

Discuss the stages that a designer would go through when coming up with a product design. Then, using a variety of products (a different one for each group), ask students to discuss questions such as *'Who is the user?'* and *'What information did the designer need to design the product?'* Take feedback from the group and conclude by asking why the user is important to the designer.

Resource and activity sheets

Introduce 'Designing products' to further illustrate the need to understand who a product is being designed for. Ask students to discuss the three groups listed on the sheet and come up with what they think each group means and what the implications are for the designer. Set the scene of a project that they are going to carry out and ask them to work in pairs to identify what they are going to design and make, and then draft a design brief in the box on the sheet.

'Carrying out research' starts to explore the need to find out the exact requirements for the design. The first part asks the students to come up with as many ways of carrying out research that they can think of. Students should initially be able to come up with some themselves, before working with a partner to come up with more. The remainder of the sheet explores the use of a questionnaire as research. You may, however, decide you also want them to carry out Internet research. You should encourage students to analyse all of their research and pick out the important parts for inclusion in a specification. Model this process using 'Writing a specification'.

Carry out a product analysis using a range of similar products (preferably between three and five) and 'Product analysis' to record the students' findings. This activity should identify that while a number of products have been produced to fulfil a need, they do so with varying success. Students should work in groups of three or five so that a consensus can be reached when scoring the products. Take feedback and question students on why they have scored the products in a certain way.

Plenary

Draw to a close by questioning students on what they have learned in the lesson. Pay particular attention to questioning them on the importance of a design brief and a specification.

Designing products

Who do we design products for?

☞ This page is going to help you to look at and understand the different people we could design for and how we would group them. The groups that we normally design for can be broken down into these three groups:

1 Ourselves 2 Clients 3 Markets

☞ What do you think these groups mean? Discuss them in small groups and write your answers in the boxes below.

Once we have decided who we are designing for we need to write a design brief that sets out what we are going to make. It might look like this: **I am going to design and make a desk tidy for my bedroom to help me organise myself when I'm doing my homework.**

☞ Now write a design brief for your own project in the box below.

Design brief:

Carrying out research

☞ Now that we know what we are going to design and make, we need to carry out research into what we could buy to do the job. Think about *'What is wrong with existing products?', 'What do people want from the type of product I am designing?'* and *'What would a suitable style and function be?'*

☞ There are a number of ways we can carry out this research, for example, a questionnaire. List as many other ways as you can think of in your workbook.

☞ A questionnaire is a good way of finding out what other people may think about your ideas and the product you are thinking of designing. Work in pairs to produce a questionnaire. A couple of hints have been provided below:

- Age range of person completing questionnaire.
- Male or female.
- Items that teenagers might need to organise in a desk tidy.
- Colours that it could be.
- How often would it be used?
- Additional functions.
- What would a reasonable cost be?

☞ To help you analyse your results, you should use options in the questionnaire that you can tick rather than ask for comments – that way you can find out what is the most popular. For example, with age you might use:

Age	8–10	☐
	11–13	☐
	14–16	☐
	17–19	☐

☞ In your workbook, design your own questionnaire to suit the needs of your design brief and start to collect your results by asking your friends to complete it.

Writing a specification

A specification sets out what the design needs to do and what it should look like – often as a list of requirements. It might look at all or a number of the following headings:

size	function (what it does)	aesthetics (how it looks)
cost	safety	environment (where it will be used)
user	ergonomics (comfort in use)	quality (materials and finish)

☞ Write a specification for a product you are designing using four of the headings above. An example of size for a desk tidy has been given:

Size – The desk tidy should be large enough to contain my pens, pencils, rubbers, pencil sharpener and ruler. It must be no bigger than 200mm x 150mm.

Product analysis

To help us come up with ideas for our designs, it is helpful to look at products that already exist and decide what makes them good or bad.

One way that you could analyse products is called **ACCESS FM** – this stands for **A**esthetics (how it looks), **C**ost, **C**ustomer (user), **E**nvironment (where it will be used), **S**afety, **S**ize, **F**unction (what it does) and **M**aterials.

☞ Using the table below, work in small groups to analyse the products given to you by your teacher and score them from zero to three. Zero is not very good. Three is excellent. Use the comment box to give your reasons.

Product	A	C	C	E	S	S	F	M	Total	Comments

Teacher's notes

Structures

Objectives

- To be able to recognise a range of structures and place them in a category based on their type
- To know that forces affect structures in different ways
- To be able to design a simple structure and test it to see what force it will withstand

Prior knowledge

Students should be able to recognise common structures that they are likely to come across in every day life.

QCA links

Unit 7d Using control to control a display – control and structures.

NC links

6) Knowledge and understanding of structures: (a).

Northern Ireland PoS

Using energy and control – mechanical systems and control d).

Scottish attainment targets

Environmental Studies – Technology
Strand – Processes and how they are applied
Level D
Environmental Studies – Skills in Technology – designing and making
Strand – Carrying out tasks
Level D

Welsh PoS

Structures: 1); 5).

Background

Students will be able to recognise that structures perform an important role in our lives and are always around us. They should group structures depending on whether they are manufactured or natural and shell or frame structures. Students will look at how the forces of compression, tension, torsion and shear affect structures in different ways, before building a simple structure and testing it to see how well it can withstand a force placed upon it.

Starter activity

Question students on what they think a structure is, before asking them to list all of the structures that they can see in and around the classroom. Once a large list has been produced, ask them to think about how they could be grouped, introducing the idea of frame and shell structures. Question students on what they think these are before asking them to group the list into those two categories. Do the same for naturally-occuring structures.

Resource and activity sheets

Provide photocopies of 'Structures' and 'Types of structure'. Briefly recap the meanings of the categories and make sure that the students can recognise the objects on the resource sheet. They should either cut out the pictures and glue them in their workbook, or draw them in the correct area of the activity sheet. It may be worth getting them to place all the pictures first and then to share their work with a partner before gluing in the pictures.

'Forces in structures' looks at the way forces can affect structures. Go through the top part of the page with the class. Try and show examples of each type of force in action. For example, a student sitting on a chair – compression; two students pulling on a rope – tension; opening a jar – torsion; cutting a piece of paper with scissors – shear; bending a piece of foam or sponge – bending. Having gone through this, ask students to identify the forces affecting the structures in the pictures on the bottom of the sheet.

Introduce shapes in structures using 'Bridge design (1)'. It may be helpful if you have drilled wooden strips with dowels on the table to enable the students to test the shapes shown. Question students on which shape they think is strongest. Ask them to use this knowledge to come up with two designs for a bridge on the activity sheet. Once completed, group students into threes and ask them to look at all of their designs and to come up with a group design which they should all draw on 'Bridge design (2)'. Students could then build and test their structures.

Plenary

Question students on what they have learned about structures and forces. Ask them to write one key point in a sentence on a sticky note and place it on the board. Pick a few notes off the board and question the students about them. This is a useful way to identify and explore misconceptions.

Structures

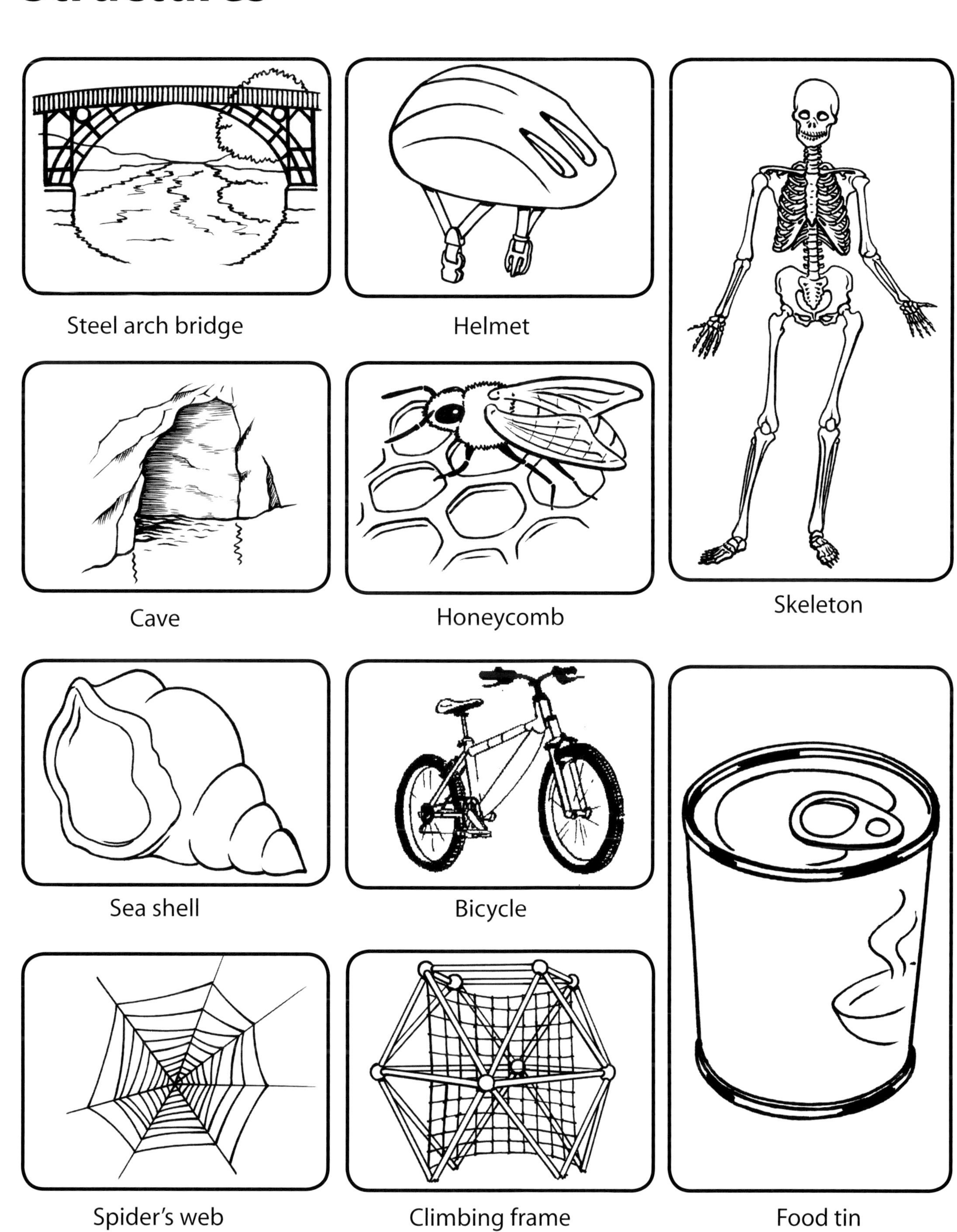

Steel arch bridge

Helmet

Skeleton

Cave

Honeycomb

Sea shell

Bicycle

Spider's web

Climbing frame

Food tin

Types of structure

We can define structures in two categories – natural and manufactured – and then classify them into frame or shell structures.

☞ Using the resource sheet, 'Structures' draw the structures into the correct area of the sheet or cut them out and glue them into a table in your workbook. One of the structures has been done for you.

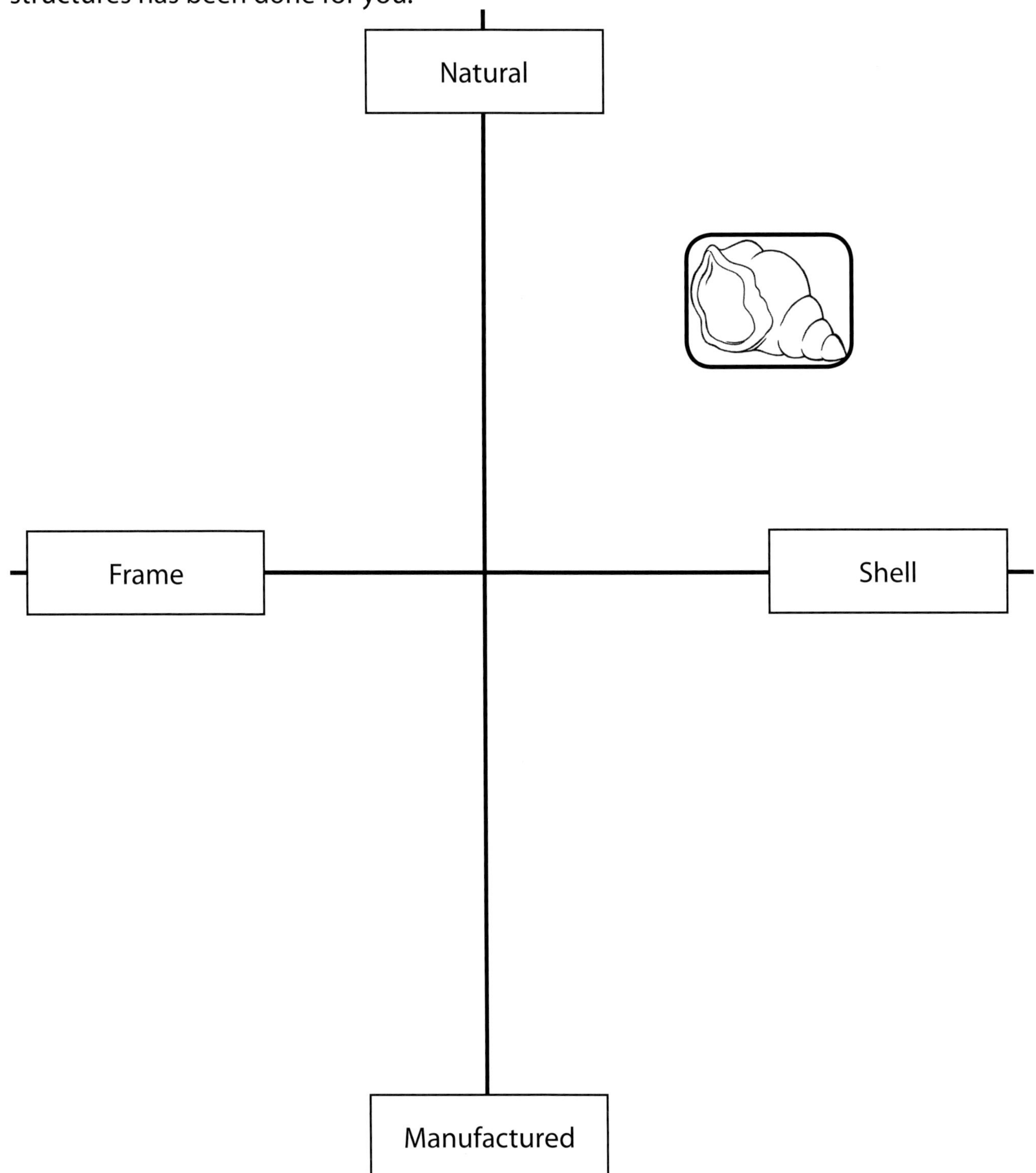

Forces in structures

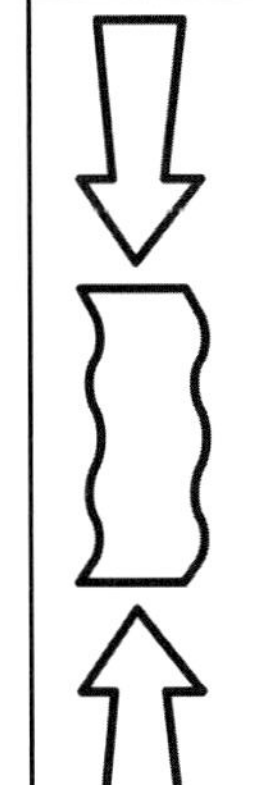

Compression

This is a squashing force. For example, the tower of a tower crane.

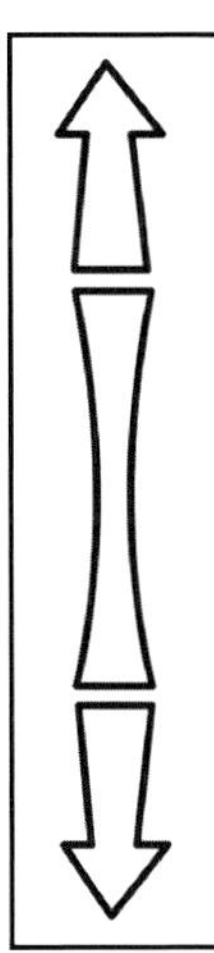

Tension

This is a pulling force. For example, the cables on a suspension bridge.

Torsion

This is a twisting force. For example, undoing a bottle cap.

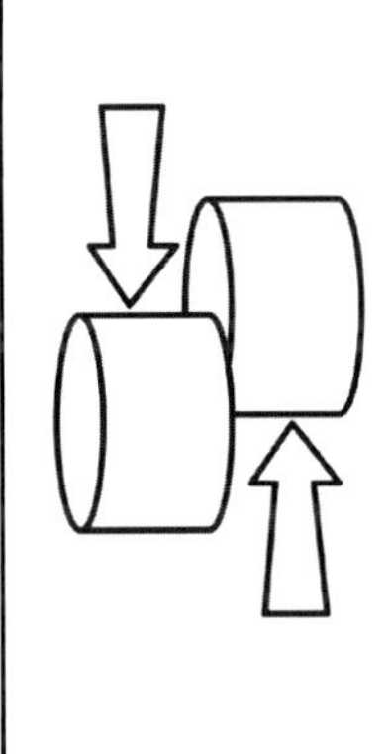

Shear

This is a force that occurs when two opposite forces try to cut a material. For example, a pair of scissors cutting paper.

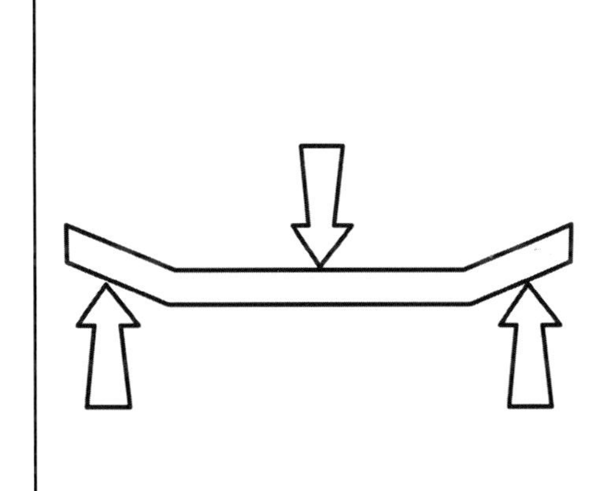

Bending

This occurs when a force is applied to a structure that is fixed at one or both ends. For example, a bridge.

☞ Working in pairs, look at the structures below and label the forces that are affecting them, using the examples above for guidance.

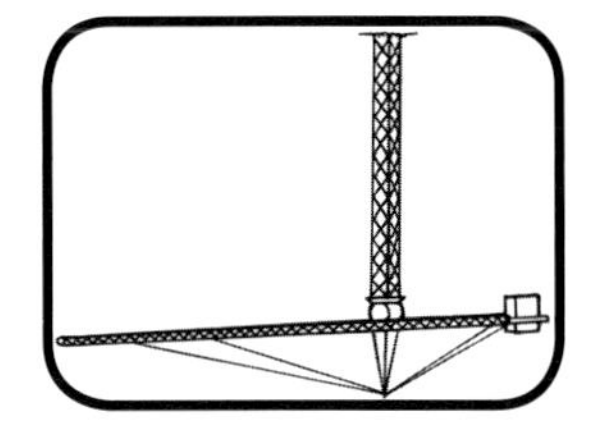

____

____

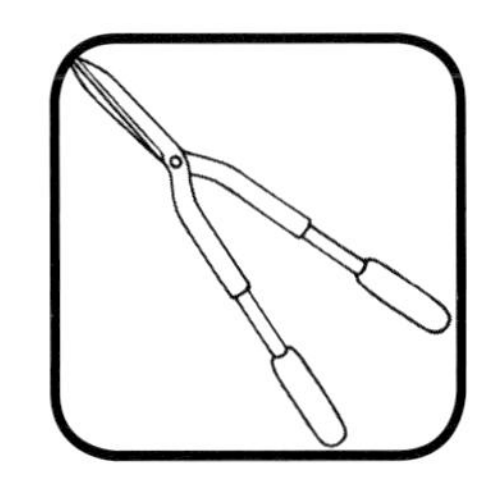

____

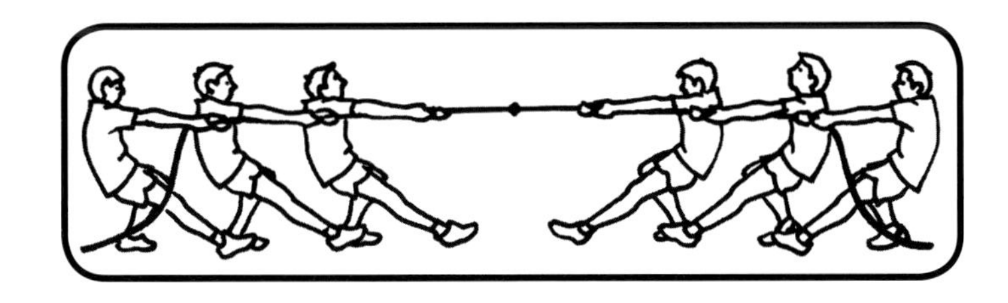

____

Bridge design (1)

Look at what can make a strong structure and then use that knowledge to design and build your own structure.

1. Look at the three shapes below. Which do you think will be the strongest?
2. Now test your prediction by using the cardboard strips and split pins provided by your teacher. Number the shapes in order of strength: one being the strongest structure and three being the weakest.

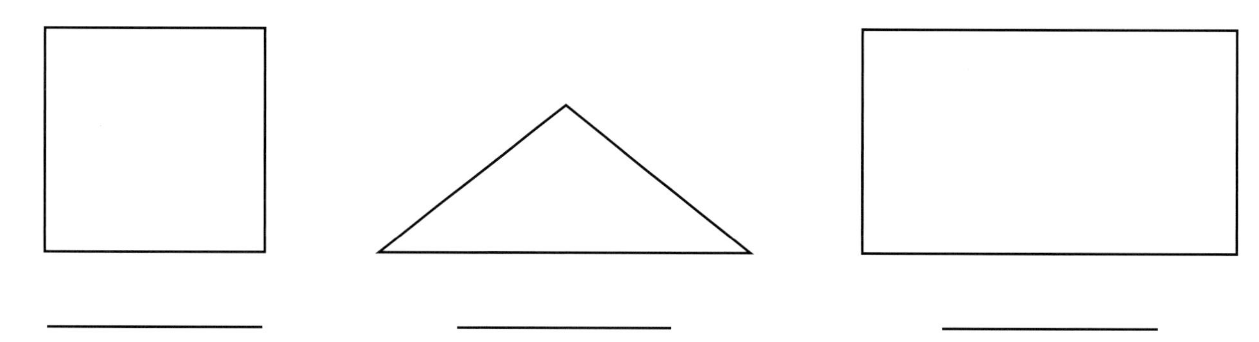

_______________ _______________ _______________

3. Now, draw two designs for a bridge that you are going to make and test.

☞ Discuss your designs with the rest of your group and pick the one you think is the strongest.

Bridge design (2)

☞ Use this page to draw your final design. Draw it as large as possible and label it to show why you have designed it in this way. Try to use the technical words from the word bank at the bottom of the page.

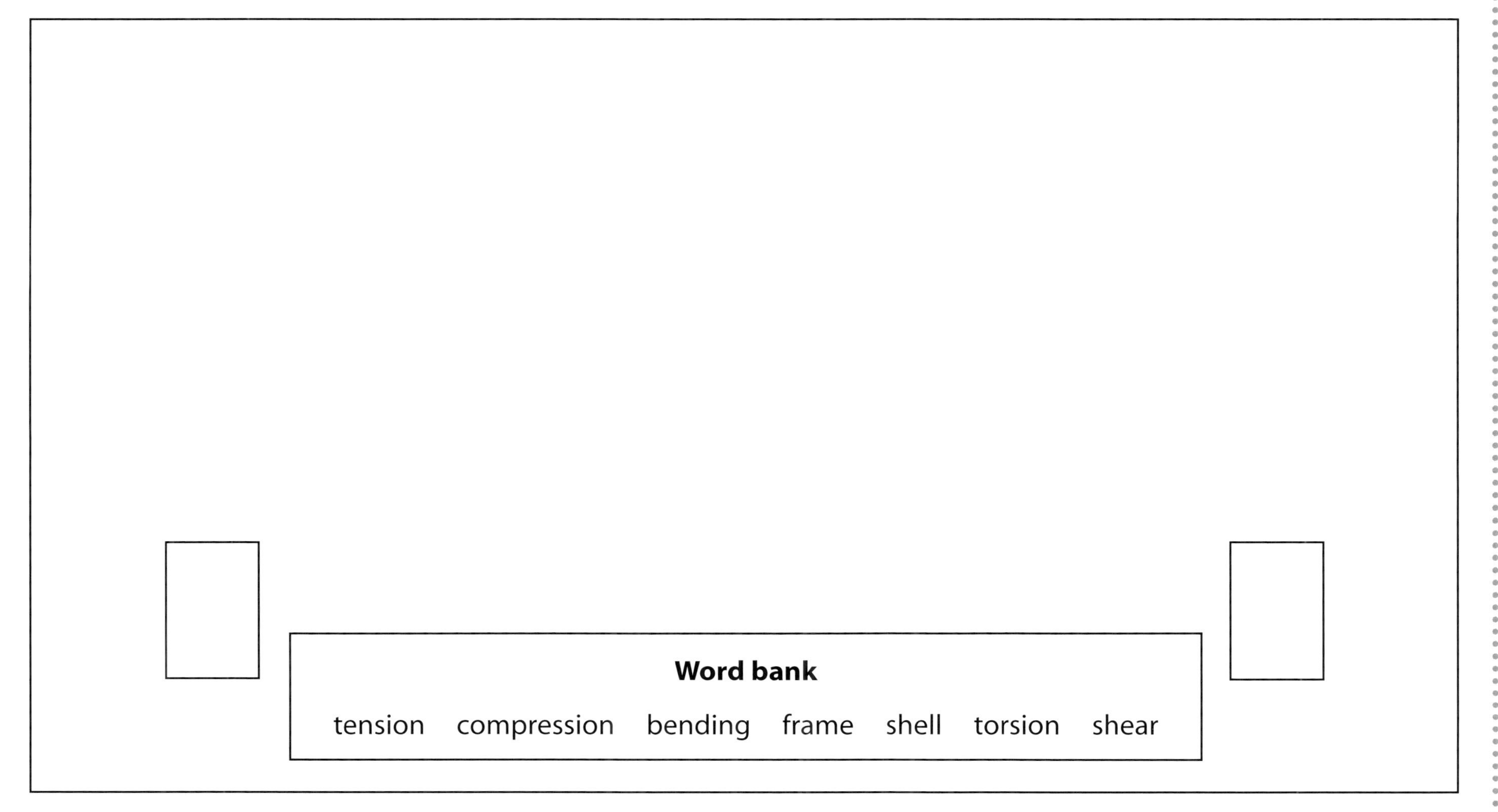

Word bank

tension compression bending frame shell torsion shear

☞ When your bridge is designed, make it in your groups before testing it to see how strong it is. Make a note of the weight it held and how you would improve your design next time.

Teacher's notes

Mechanisms

Objectives

- To know and understand that a mechanism is a system that converts one type of movement into another
- To be able to recognise the different components that make up simple mechanisms
- To use mechanisms in a simple design project

Prior knowledge

To achieve these objectives, students should be able to recognise items that contain simple mechanisms and be able to discuss how they work.

QCA links

Unit 7d Using control to control a display – control and structures.

NC links

5) Knowledge and understanding of systems and control: d).

Northern Ireland PoS

Using energy and control – mechanical systems and control.

Scottish attainment targets

Environmental Studies – Technology
Strand – Processes and how they are applied
Level D
Environmental Studies – Skills in Technology – designing and making
Strand – Carrying out tasks
Level D

Welsh PoS

Systems and Control: 1); 6).

Background

Many products that students will come into contact with will involve some form of movement or motion. This unit intends to explore mechanisms and how they are systems which convert different types of movement. Mechanisms can contain movement produced by a range of components including levers, gears and cams. Linking this unit to a simple project including mechanisms such as an automata, enables students to explore the concepts in practice.

Starter activity

Question students on what they think a mechanism is. Try to give them time to think about the question and discuss it with a partner before sharing their answer with the class. To aid this, give small groups different questions based on mechanisms and movement and take whole class feedback from each group, before asking them to think of products that contain mechanisms.

Resource and activity sheets

Introduce 'Common mechanisms', which shows a number of different products that include mechanisms. Hopefully, some will have already been identified. Go through the sheet as a class to ensure that all the students understand what the products are and how the mechanisms work.

'Gear ratios' explores the use of gears and how they can be used to control speed. Introduce ratios to the group and go through the top half of the sheet as a class. It would be helpful if the students can have access to Lego® kits that contain the gears specified on the sheets as this will help them to work out the ratios. Using the first one as an example, show how the gears mesh and how by turning the input, the output turns in the opposite direction and at a different rate. Students should then complete the remainder of the sheet, working in small groups. Go through the answers as a class and show how the ratios can be worked out through division.

Introduce 'Levers' by demonstrating the use of levers in the classroom. For this you will need a length of timber, a block to use as a pivot and an object to use as a load. Use a student as the effort to show how the lever can be used. Do this for all three classes of lever. Ask students to discuss the pictures shown on the sheet and decide which class of lever each picture is showing.

The second resource sheet, 'Cams', introduces cams and how they could be used in an automata. Go through this sheet as a class before asking the students to come up with their own idea for an automata on 'Designing a child's automata toy'.

Plenary

Set different groups a task to present what they have understood about one of the areas covered in this unit to the remainder of the class. The class should then ask questions on the unit to the group presenting.

Common mechanisms

What are mechanisms? A mechanism is a system which converts one type of movement into another. It can contain **levers**, **cams**, **gears** or **pulleys**. The mechanism can contain just one gear or lever or a group of linked components.

It can convert linear movement (something that moves in a straight line) to rotary movement (something that moves round and round) or the other way around.

For example, the wheels on a bike are a rotary movement that make the bike travel in a linear direction.

☞ These are all types of mechanisms. Can you think what components they use for their mechanisms?

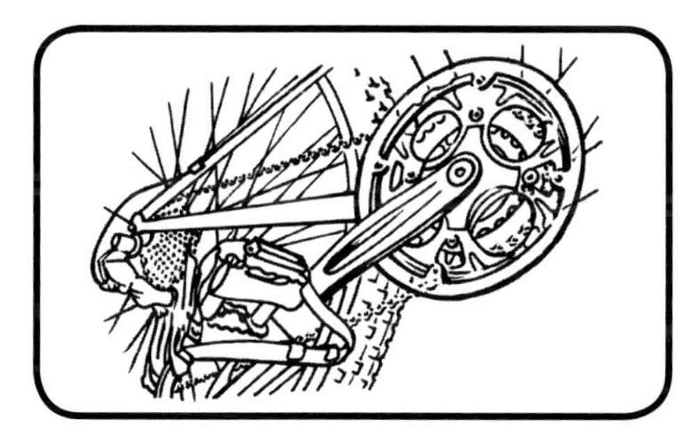

A mountain bike uses gears to make it easier to go up hills or go faster.

A sack truck uses levers to make it easier to move heavy objects.

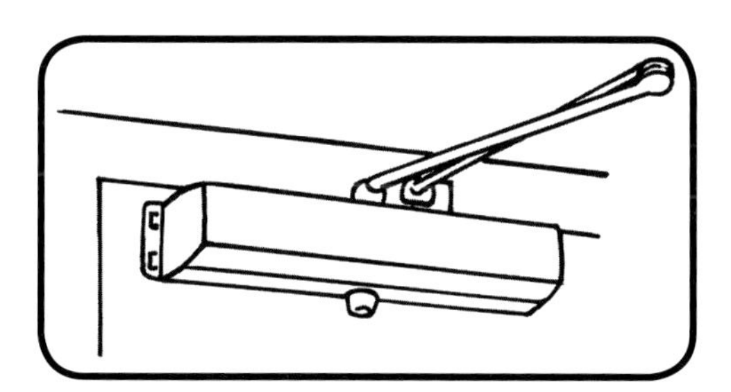

A door closure uses levers to control the speed a door closes.

A see-saw uses levers for fun.

An automata converts rotary motion into linear movement using cams.

Gear ratios

To control the speed of the electrical buggy, like the one shown, we have to work out the speed of the output from the gear box that is connected to the motor. To do this, we use something called gear ratios. Work in pairs to complete this sheet. You may find it helpful to use Lego® gears to make the gear trains shown.

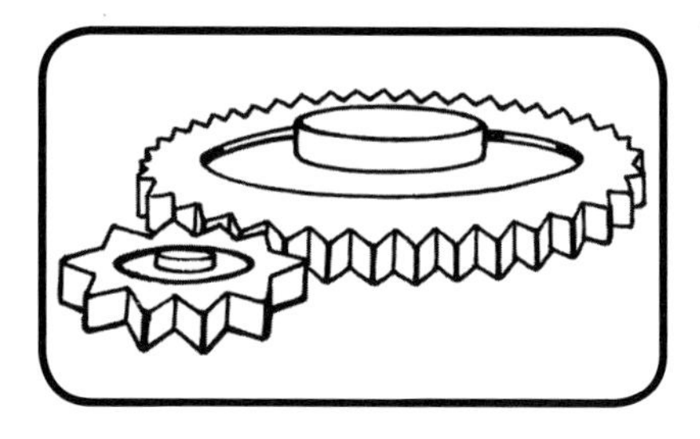

To work out gear ratios we need to know how many teeth are on each gear. The gears in the picture have 40 and ten teeth. If the input gear was the one with 40 teeth and the output the one with ten teeth, the gear ratio would be 1:4. This means that for each turn of the input gear, the output will turn four times, making the output faster than the input.

As it is hard to draw gears showing all of their teeth, we can draw them like this, with the number inside showing how many teeth each gear has. To make a gear train, we overlap the gears as shown.

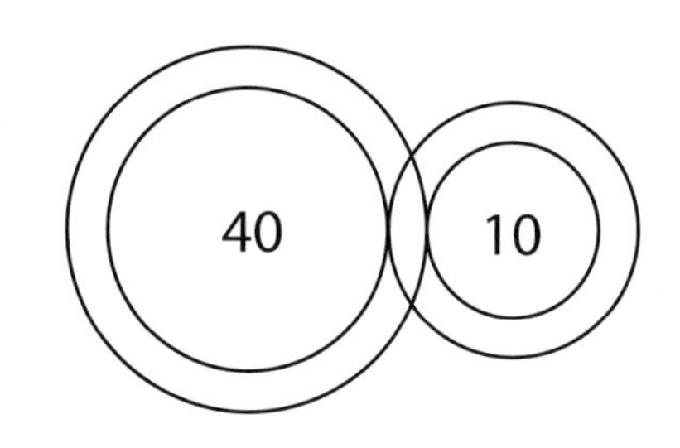

☞ In your pairs, work out the gear ratios for the gears shown below. The first one has been done for you. Test your answers using the Lego® kits provided.

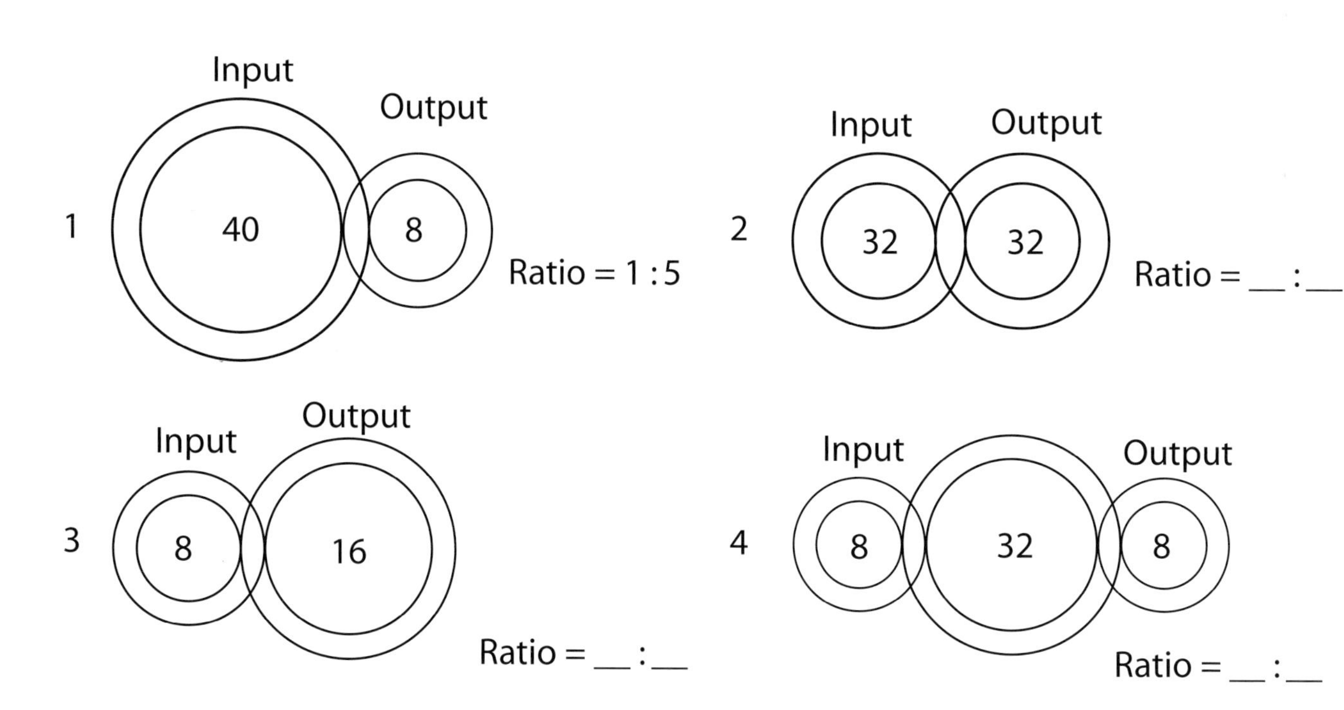

Levers

Levers can be used to help us move heavy objects. All levers are made up of a fulcrum (or pivot), an effort and a load. This is shown in the example below.

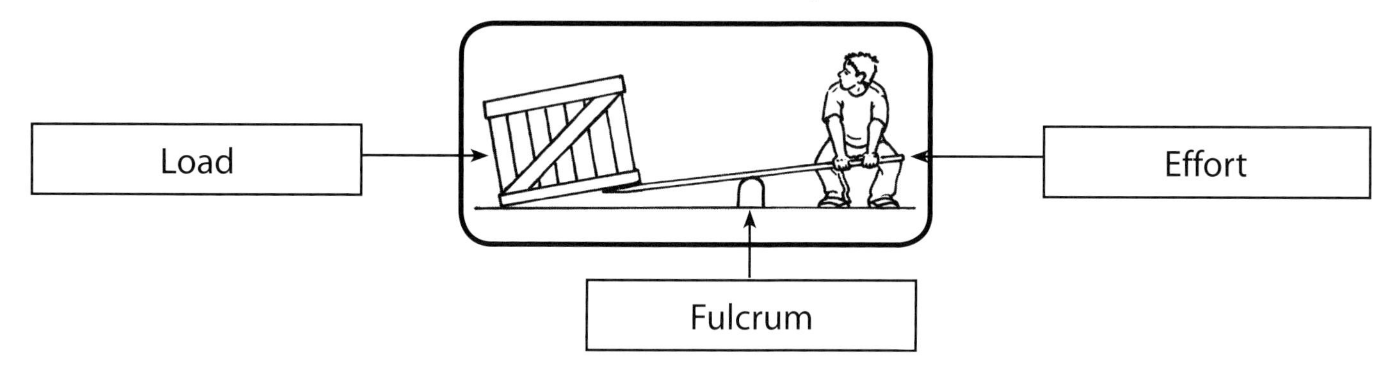

Levers are broken down into three classes that depend on where the load is in relation to the fulcrum and effort.

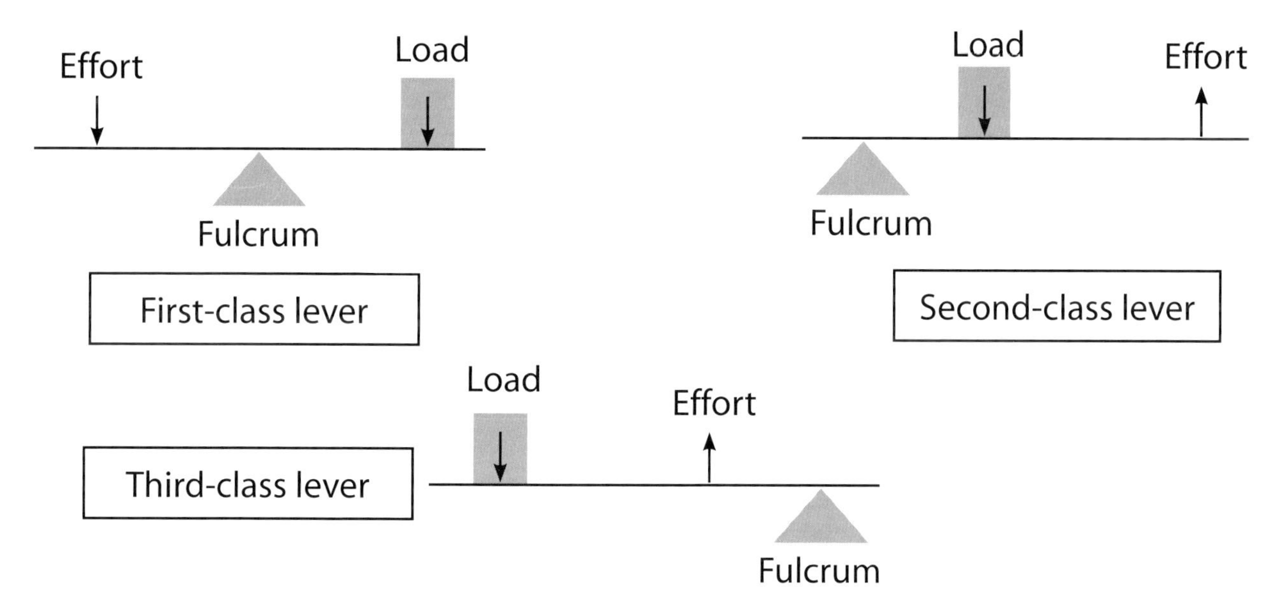

☞ The pictures below show common items that use levers. Can you tell what class they are? Work in pairs to decide and then write the correct class next to the picture. The first one has been done for you.

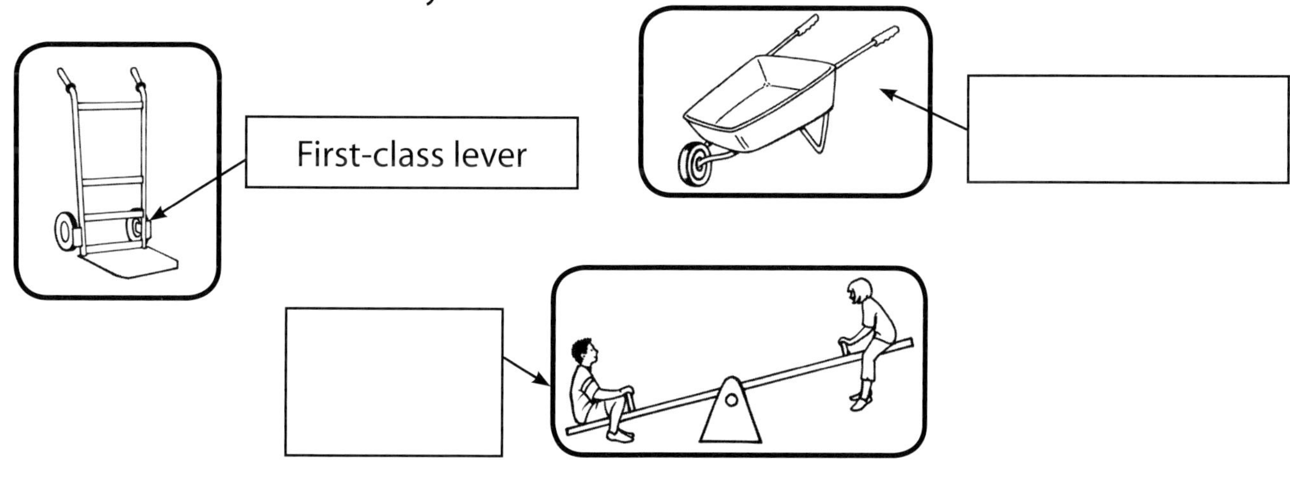

Cams

Sometimes we can use cams and followers in our projects to produce movement.

How do they work?

As the cam turns, the follower will rise and fall. The speed rises and falls depending on the shape of the cam.

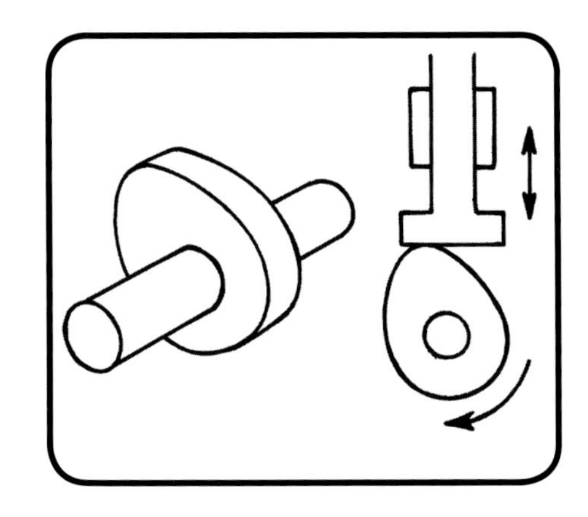

The three most common shaped cams are shown below.

Pear cam

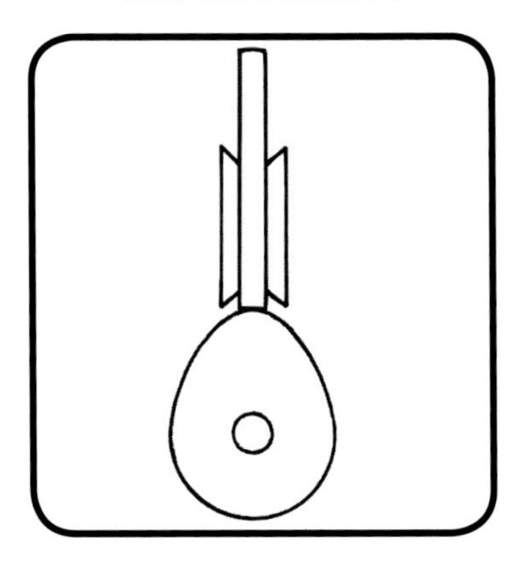

As the cam rotates, the follower stays level for half a rotation, then it rises and falls following the cam profile.

Eccentric cam

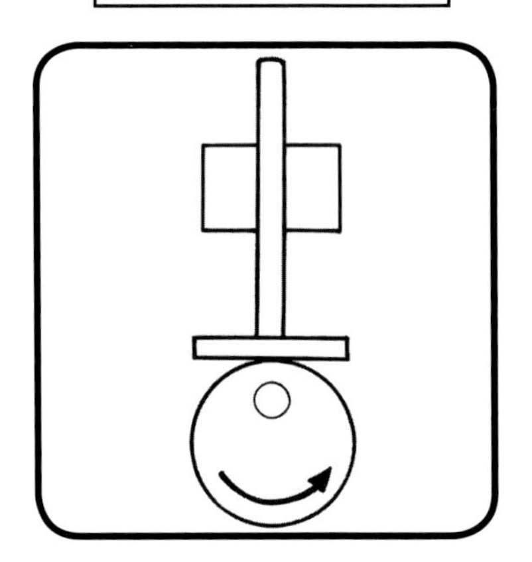

The follower moves up and down in a vertical direction. Its movement is very smooth.

Snail cam

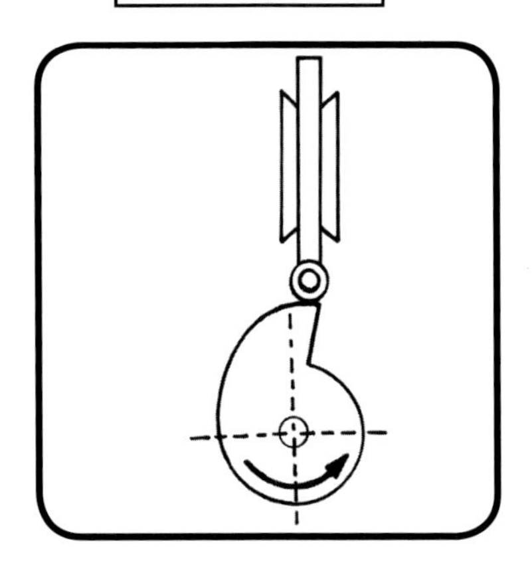

As the snail cam rotates, the follower stays level for a short time. It then rises slowly and suddenly drops.

Here are some examples of toys using each type of cam:

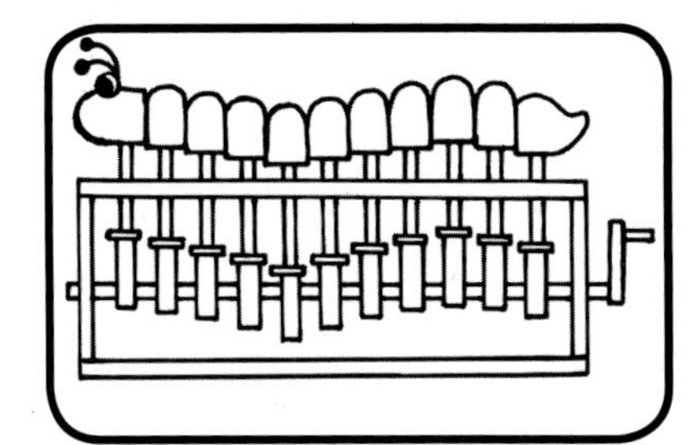

Designing a child's automata toy

☞ Design a child's automata toy such as those on 'Cams', using two different types of cam.

Teacher's notes

Tools and equipment

Objectives

- To be able to recognise a variety of workshop tools
- To be able to select appropriate tools for given tasks
- To be able to use workshop equipment and tools in a safe manner

Prior knowledge

To achieve the objectives of this unit, students should be able to recognise common tools.

QCA links

Unit 8b (ii) Designing for clients – resistant materials.

NC links

2) Working with tools, equipment, materials and components to produce quality products: a).

Northern Ireland PoS

Manufacturing a).

Scottish attainment targets

Environmental Studies – Technology
Strand – Needs and how they are met
Level D
Strand – Resources and how they are managed
Level E
Strand – Processes and how they are applied
Environmental Studies – Skills in Technology – designing and making
Strand – Preparing for tasks
Level E

Welsh PoS

Making skills: 2).

Background

To enable students to gain the most from working within Design and Technology, they must know and understand how to use the tools and equipment in a safe manner. This unit will enable students to recognise the different tools and equipment that they will use in their lessons and through demonstrations, learn to use it correctly and safely.

Starter activity

Prior to the lesson, place one of each tool that the students will be using on each desk. When the students enter, tell them to sit down without touching anything. Ask them to name the tools and discuss what they think each is used for. Take responses from each group before asking them to look around the room and to identify the equipment that they can see. Discuss safety with the group and come up with an agreed set of rules for the workshop.

Resource and activity sheets

Give the students the resource sheet 'Common workshop tools' so that they can refer to it during their future work.

'Safety with workshop equipment' enables you to record students' safe use of the machines that they are likely to use in the workshop. To show that they can use it safely, sign off each item on the sheet after a student has used it. Also, ask the students to explain on the sheet what the equipment was used for.

'Selecting tools and equipment (1)' asks students to think about the tools and equipment they might need to use in order to make a simple picture puzzle and how these tools would be used. Encourage the students to explain their use in as much detail as possible. They should include the part it is used on and whether it is used to cut a straight line or a detailed shape and so on.

To further reinforce and explore their knowledge and understanding of the tools and processes used in making a product, ask the students to complete 'Selecting tools and equipment (2)' after they have used each tool while making a project of their own.

Use 'Tools quiz' to see what they have remembered. The students should work through this individually before going through it as a class and correcting their responses.

Plenary

To draw this lesson to a close, gather a number of the tools covered in the lesson and ask students to identify them. Try to gain from students what the tools are used for, how they are used and the materials that they are suitable or unsuitable to use on.

Common workshop tools

Hand drill

Coping saw

Chisel

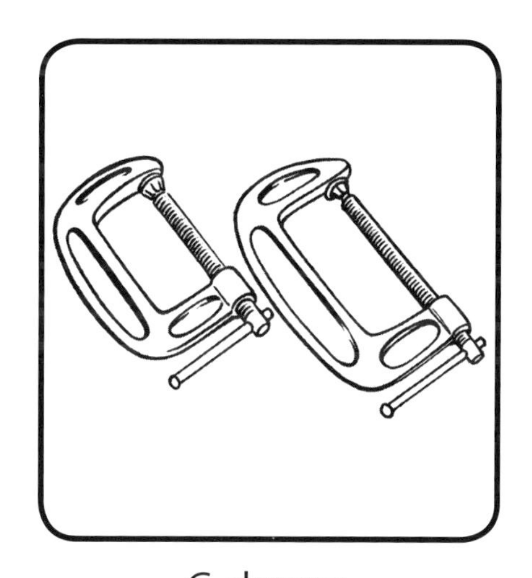

G clamps

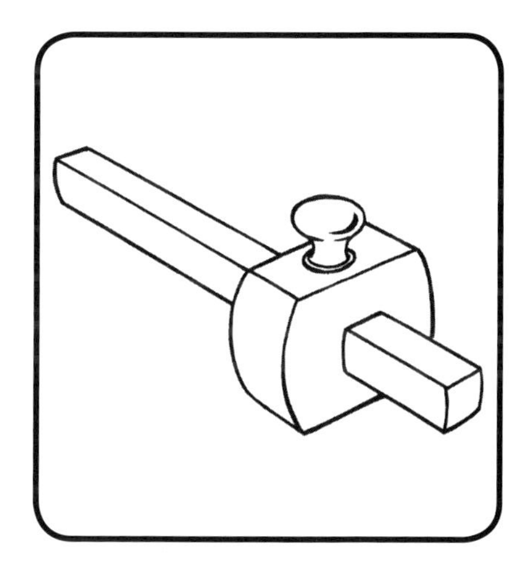

Marking gauge

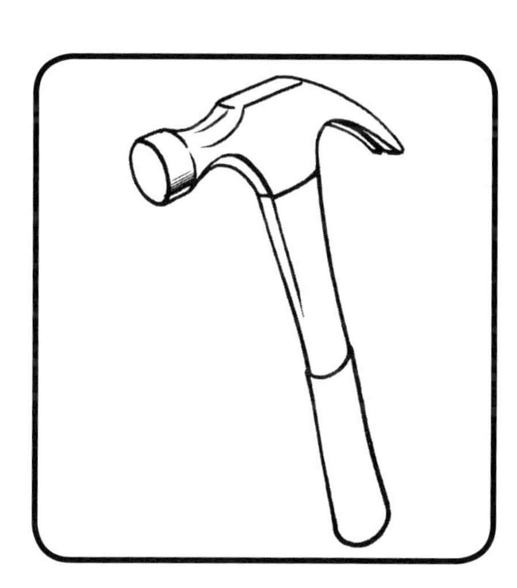

Hammer

Tenon saw

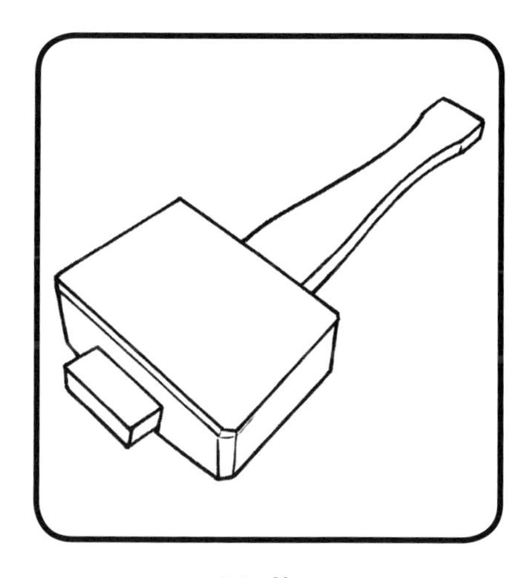

Mallet

Try square

Safety with workshop equipment

As well as hand tools, you will come into contact with a number of machines in the workshop.

Make sure you know how to use these machines safely.

☞ Complete this sheet as you are taught to use each machine. Explain how you have used each one and what you have used them for. One example has been provided for you.

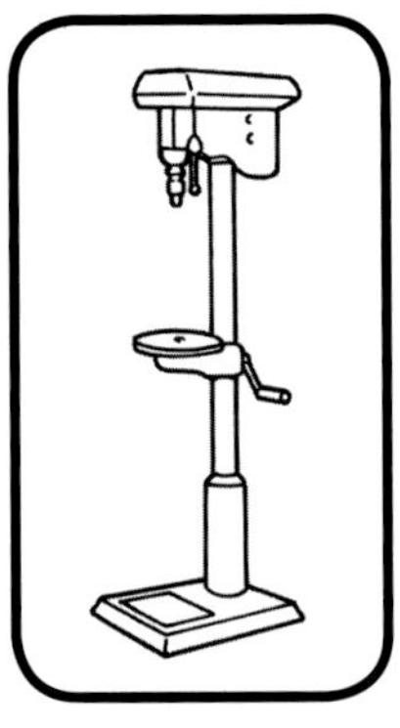

Pedestal drill – I used this to drill holes in the pieces of my picture puzzle in order to fit small dowels that make them easier to lift out. Wearing goggles and an apron, I selected the right-sized drill and fitted it in the chuck using the chuck key. I made sure my work was lined up and held secure before switching on and using the handle to lower the drill into the material.

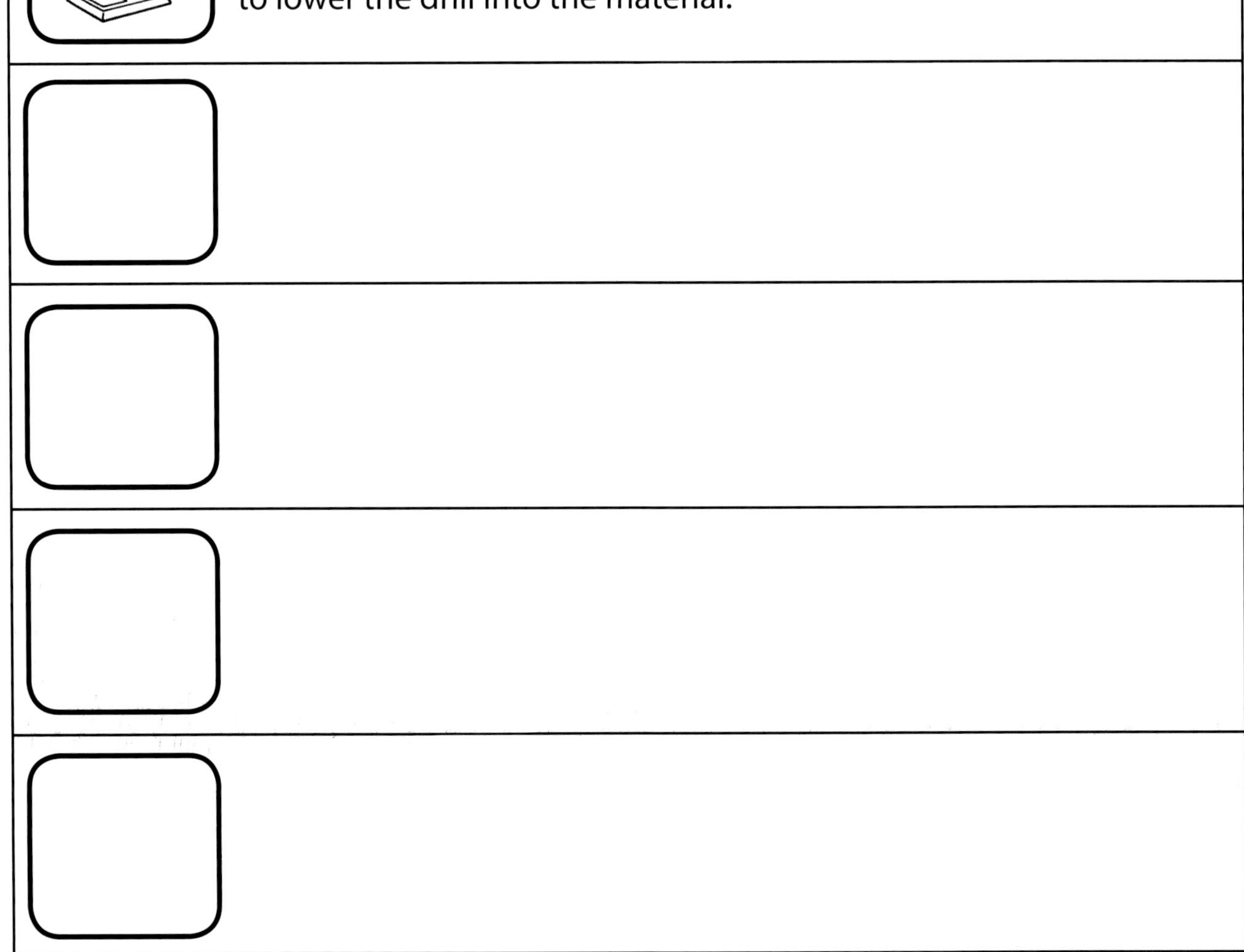

Selecting tools and equipment (1)

☞ Using the resource sheet, 'Common workshop tools', draw the tools in the order that you would use them to make the wooden puzzle shown. Explain how you would use each tool.

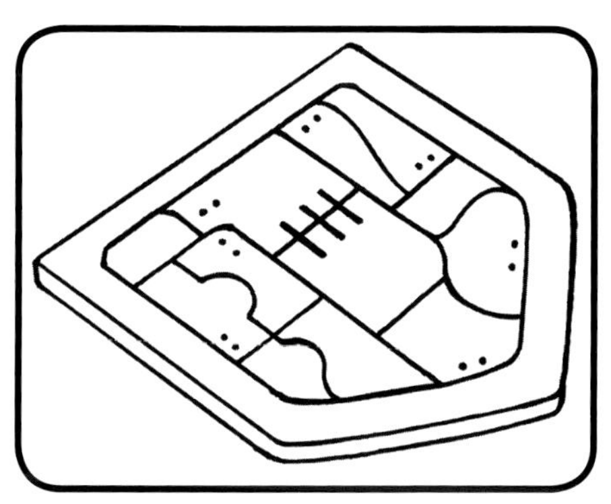

Tool	How it would be used

Selecting tools and equipment (2)

☞ Use this sheet to select the tools and equipment that you are going to use to make a project of your own.

I am making a ______________________________.

This is the equipment I am going to be using.

Tool	How it is going to be used

Tools quiz

Name the tools and equipment shown and explain how each would be used.

Tool	Tool name	How it would be used
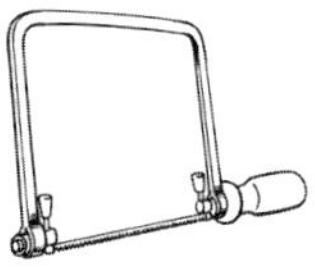		
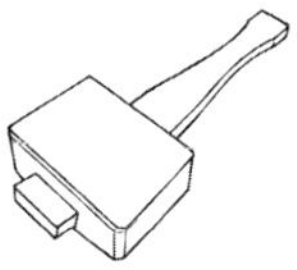		

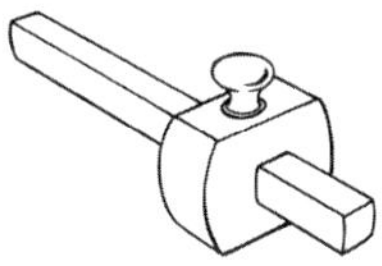		
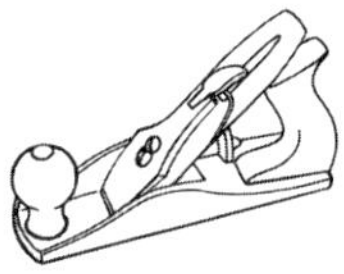		
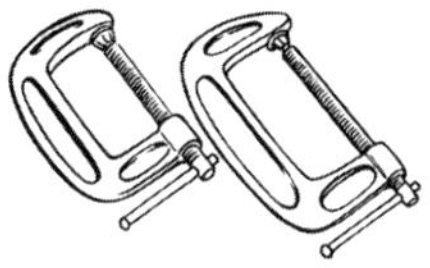		
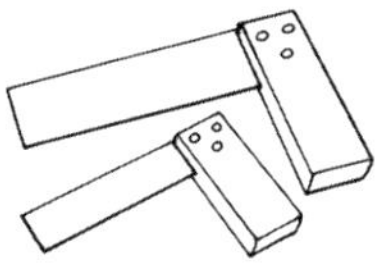		
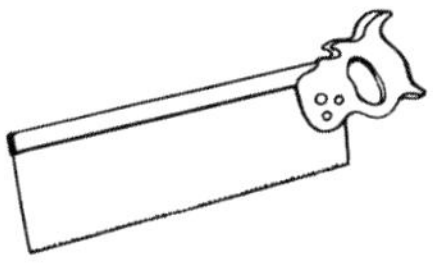		
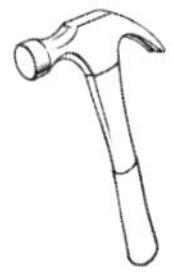		
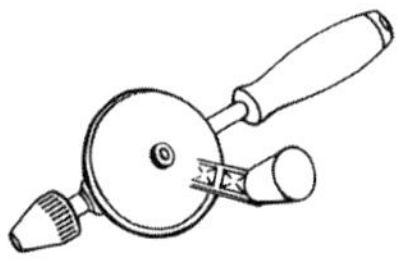		

Teacher's notes

Joining and finishing materials

Objectives

- To gain knowledge and understanding of a variety of techniques for joining and combining materials
- To know that finishes need to be applied to protect products and ensure they are attractive to the user
- To be able to select an appropriate finish for a given product

Prior knowledge

To achieve the objectives of this unit, students should be able to build upon their personal knowledge of how common products are made. They should also be aware of how products can be damaged if they are not protected.

QCA links

Unit 8a (ii) Exploring materials – resistant materials.

NC links

2) Working with tools, equipment, materials and components to produce quality products: (c).

Northern Ireland PoS

Manufacturing d).

Scottish attainment targets

Environmental Studies – Technology
Strand – Processes and how they are applied
Level D
Strand – Needs and how they are met
Level D
Environmental Studies – Skills in Technology – designing and making
Strand – Carrying out tasks
Level E

Welsh PoS

Materials skills: 2); 5).

Background

As most products contain more than one component, it is important that students are taught ways in which they can be combined that are suitable to the material they are using and the product they are making. As a final stage of the making process, a high-quality finish must be achieved, again, as there are a range of finishes to choose from, depending on the materials and the product. Students need to be taught how to select the appropriate finish for the product they are producing.

Starter activity

Using a variety of products, question students on how the different parts are joined. Try to select products that include some of the joining methods on the resource sheet 'Joining materials'. Expand the questioning to examine the finishes on the products and what the students think the reasons for the finishes are.

Resource and activity sheets

Introduce the resource sheet 'Joining materials' to the students, showing the common methods of joining that they are likely to use in their project work. Go through this sheet as a class and add any additional joining methods that the students may need, depending on the projects they will be involved in.

'Joints and their uses' looks at four examples of products and asks the students to name the type of joint they would find on each one and then to explain their answers. Allow students to work in pairs to complete this activity before taking responses from the whole group.

'Finishing materials' introduces a range of finishing products and techniques. Before handing out the sheet, go through the finishes with the class, asking the students to describe the type of finish and the product that each finish could be used for. Then give the sheet out and explain the task to the students.

To reinforce the whole finishing process, use 'The finishing process' to show the procedure that could be used for finishing a CD rack. The students should number the processes from one to six; the first has been done for them. They should be able to complete this on their own before going through it as a class and questioning their reasons.

The students should then be able to complete 'Finishing in practice' as they are working on a project of their own, to explain how they are finishing their product and how this will improve the quality of it.

Plenary

Question students on why finishes are used and why different finishes are suitable for different products. Use a range of product photographs to test their knowledge about the suitability of finishes and ask them to name a product and finish.

Joining materials

Butt joint

Butt joints are quick and simple to use but lack strength.

Dovetail joint

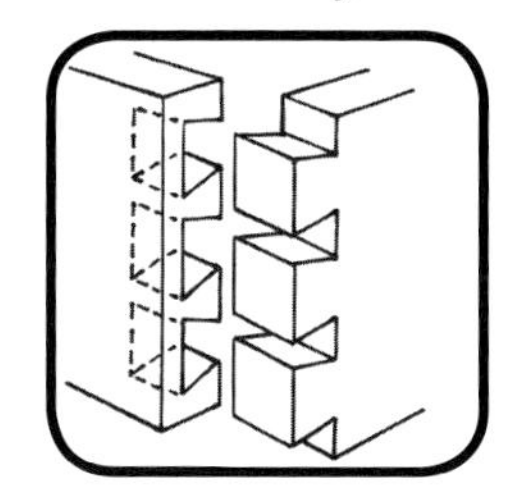

Dovetail joints are very strong and attractive to look at.

Lap joint

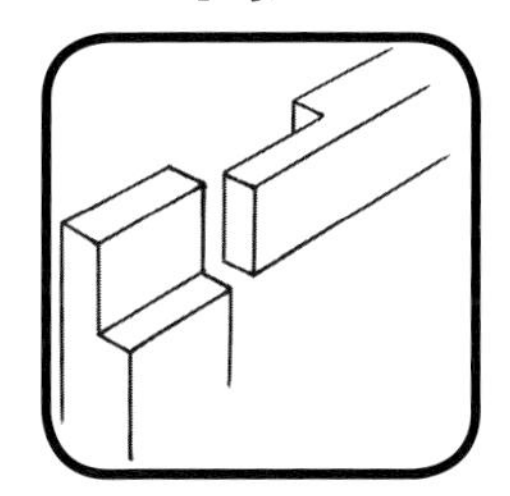

Lap joints are stronger and neater than butt joints, with less end grain showing.

Mortise and tenon joint

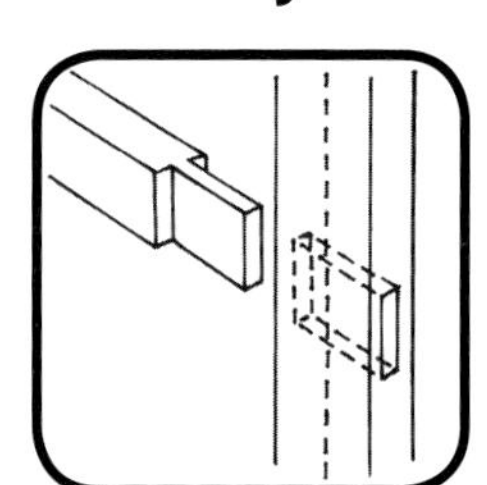

The mortise and tenon joint is used to make frames.

Mitre joint

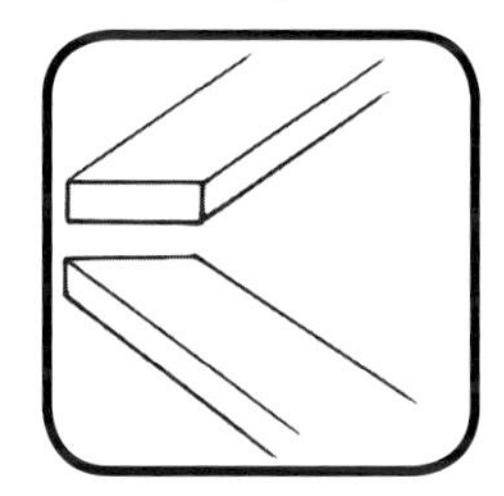

A neat and simple joint to make with no end grain showing. Often used on picture frames.

Knock down fittings

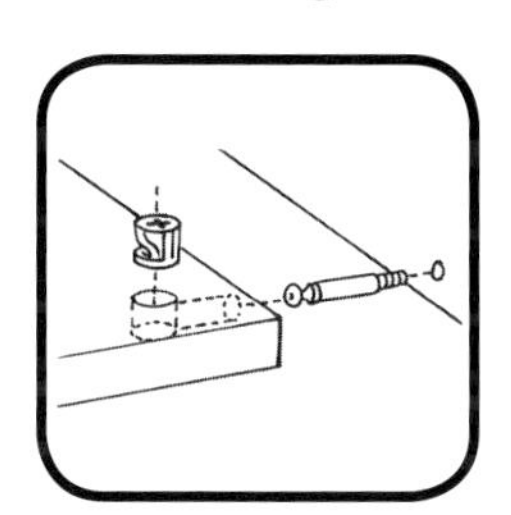

These fittings are simple and easy to use and are often found on flat pack furniture for easy assembly.

Brazing

Brazing uses gas to heat the metals to be joined and melts the brazing rods to fill the joint. Flux must be used to help the brazing rod flow.

Solvent cement

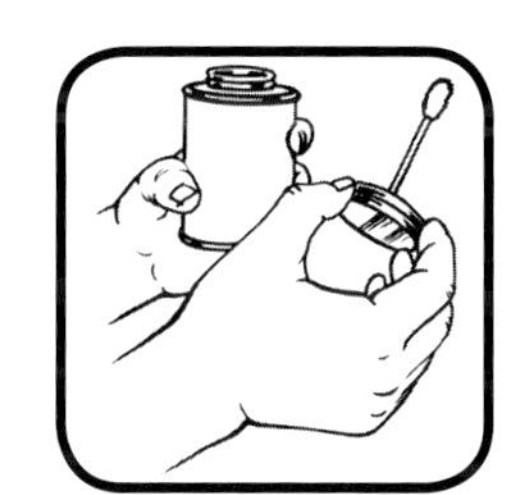

This is a liquid that chemically joins the plastics together. Careful use can result in a very smooth joint.

Arc welding

A welding power supply is used to create an electric arc by striking the welding rod against the material. Lifting it off slightly burns away the flux coating and enables the rod to melt into the gap between the materials, joining them together.

Nuts and bolts

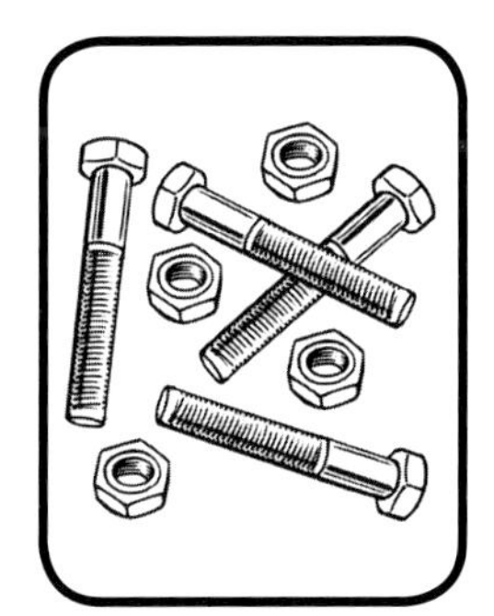

A common way to join materials temporarily.

Joints and their uses

☞ Look at the pictures below and decide what methods of joining have been used on each. Write this in the box connected to each picture and explain your choice.

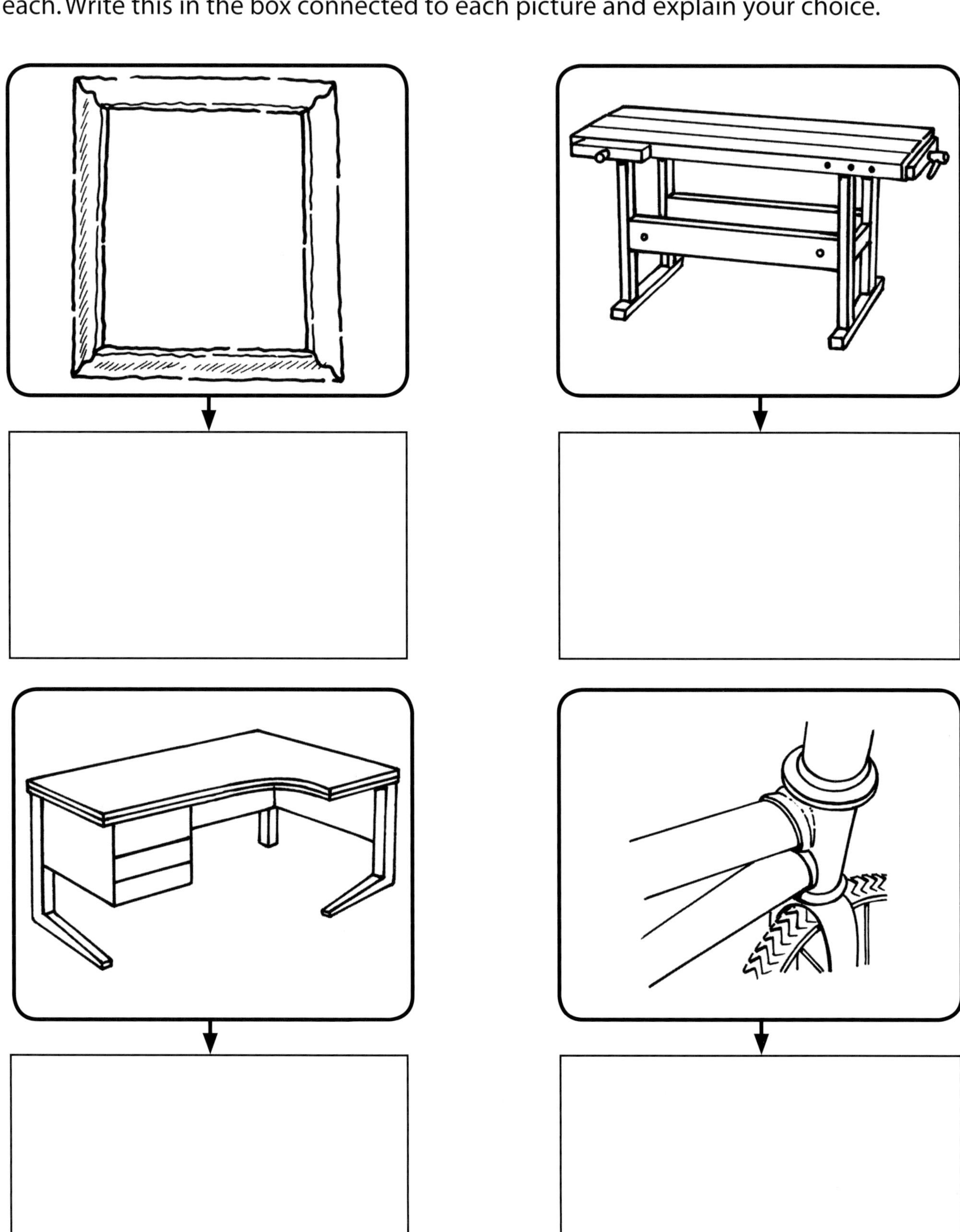

Finishing materials

Finishing is the last stage of the making process. If the finish is not very good, it is unlikely that anyone would buy the product even if it was well made. The finish doesn't just make the product look good, it also protects it from getting damaged. For example, wood can rot if allowed to absorb moisture or left outside unprotected, while metals can corrode and rust.

☞ Look at the pictures below and try to match the finishes to the products. Try to explain your reasons for these choices in the boxes next to the objects.

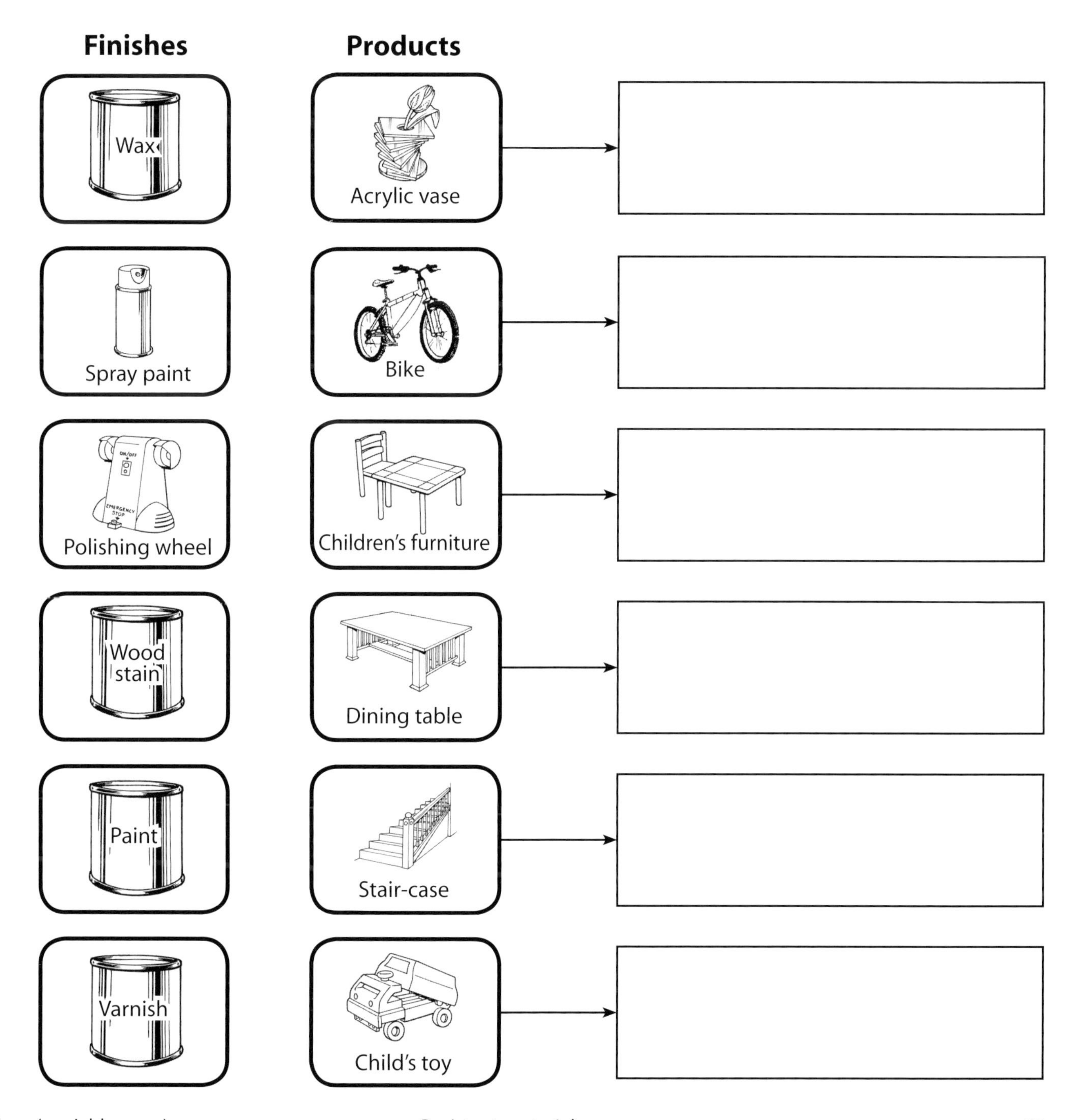

The finishing process

Before the final finish is applied, it is important to ensure that the product is as smooth as possible.

☞ The objects below relate to the most common stages in the finishing process. Can you number them in the order that you would use them if you were making the finished product in the centre? The first one has been done for you.

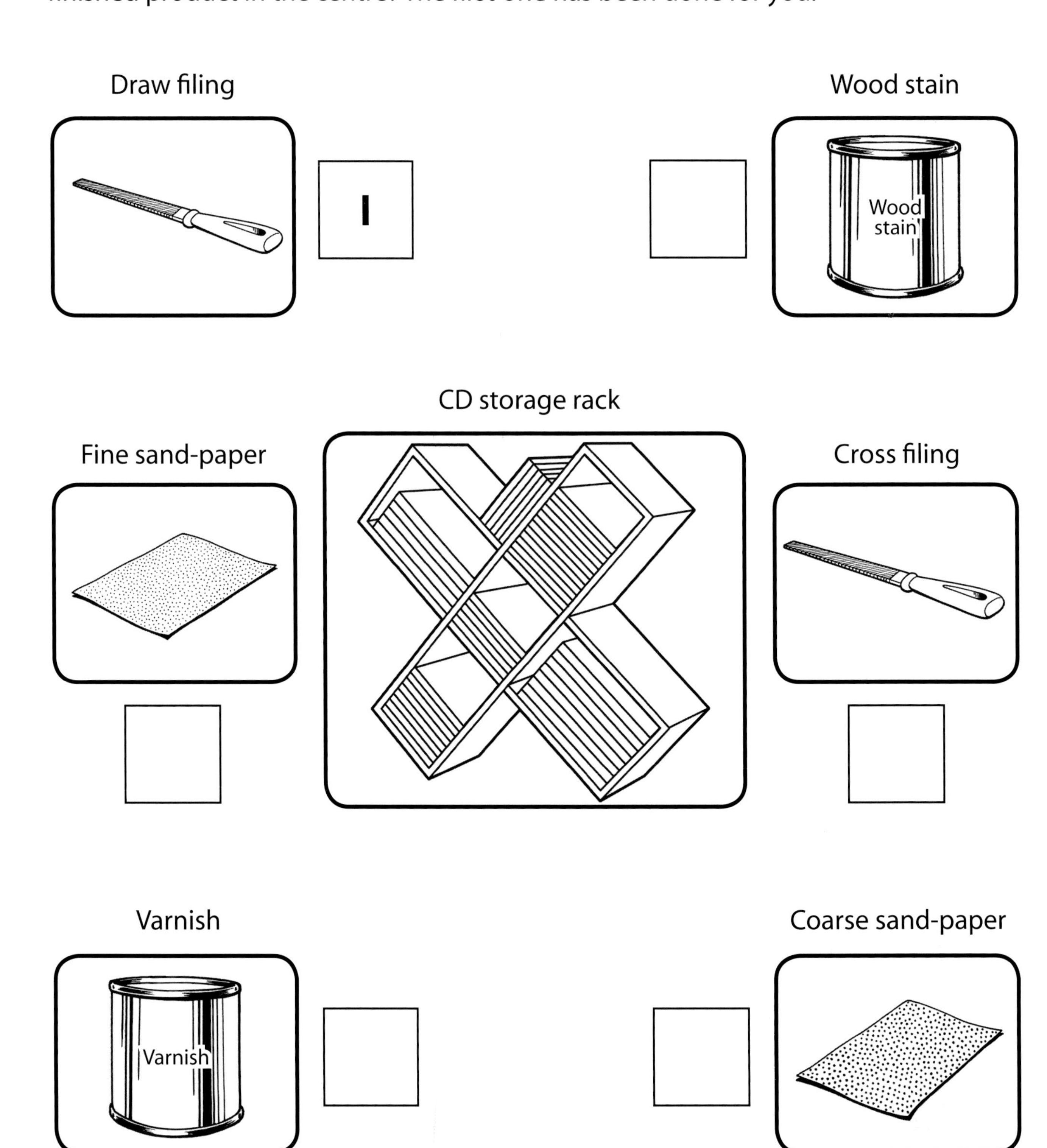

Finishing in practice

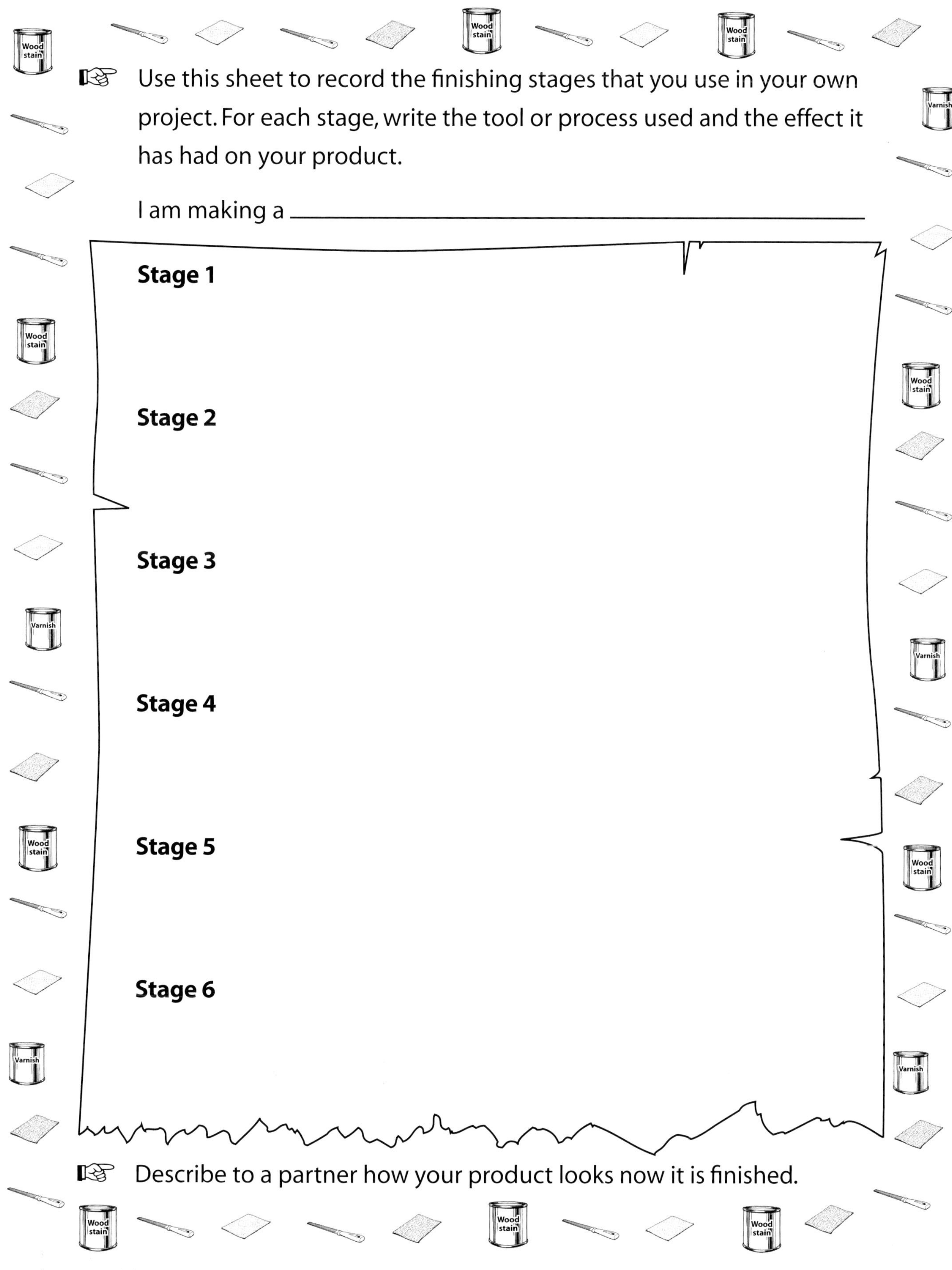

☞ Use this sheet to record the finishing stages that you use in your own project. For each stage, write the tool or process used and the effect it has had on your product.

I am making a ______________________________

Stage 1

Stage 2

Stage 3

Stage 4

Stage 5

Stage 6

☞ Describe to a partner how your product looks now it is finished.

Teacher's notes

Production methods

Objectives

- To understand that batch production is a method of making a small number of identical products
- To be able to identify common methods of batch production
- To know the advantages of making products in batches

Prior knowledge

To achieve these objectives, it is helpful if students are familiar with kits such as Lego® and classroom equipment that can be used for batch production, such as the vacuum former.

QCA links

Unit 8e (ii) Producing batches – resistant materials.

NC links

2) Working with tools, equipment, materials and components to produce quality products: (d).

Northern Ireland PoS

Knowledge and understanding – manufacturing materials, components, techniques and processes.

Scottish attainment targets

Environmental Studies – Technology
Strand – Needs and how they are met
Level D
Strand – Processes and how they are applied
Level C
Environmental Studies – Skills in Technology – designing and making
Strand – Carrying out tasks
Level E

Welsh PoS

Material skills: 6).

Background

As most products are made in quantity in industry, students need to be aware of how these products are produced and some of the techniques used. This is a good opportunity to introduce vacuum forming which is commonly used in Design and Technology workshops.

Starter activity

Write 'one-off production', 'batch production' and 'continuous production' on the board. Ask the students to discuss these terms and question students about processes they may be familiar with, such as vacuum forming in the classroom, the way that they make prototype products and industrial processes such as car manufacturing. Ask the students what category each process fits into.

Resource and activity sheets

The resource sheet 'Vacuum forming process' goes through the process of vacuum forming in detail. Go through this with the class. If possible, demonstrate this process, reinforcing the stages identified on the resource sheet.

Introduce 'One-off and batch production (1)' and '(2)'. To complete these tasks you will need sufficient model kits to enable the students to produce a number of the same product. The students should first produce the product on their own, timing how long it takes. Ask the students to multiply this to find out how long it would take to produce 20. Put the students into groups of five and explain that they are going to form a production line and that they will all need to fulfil a role. Ask the students to complete the first part of sheet two identifying who is going to do what in their production group. They should then begin producing the products in their groups, timing how long it takes to make 20 of the product. Once they have finished, ask the students to fill in the remainder of the sheet. Question groups on how they found the activity and which production method was faster.

'Using jigs' examines how jigs can be used to manufacture components accurately. Go through the top section of the page as a group, asking the students to complete the diagram. The remainder of the sheet asks students to come up with a design for a jig to help them in a project they are working on. Encourage students to think about elements they have found difficult and how these could have been made easier.

Use 'Matching products to processes' to reinforce this unit and introduce students to methods of production that they may not have come across so far, such as blow moulding.

Plenary

Give a number of groups a different method of production. The students should come up with three questions about that method to ask another group.

Vacuum forming process

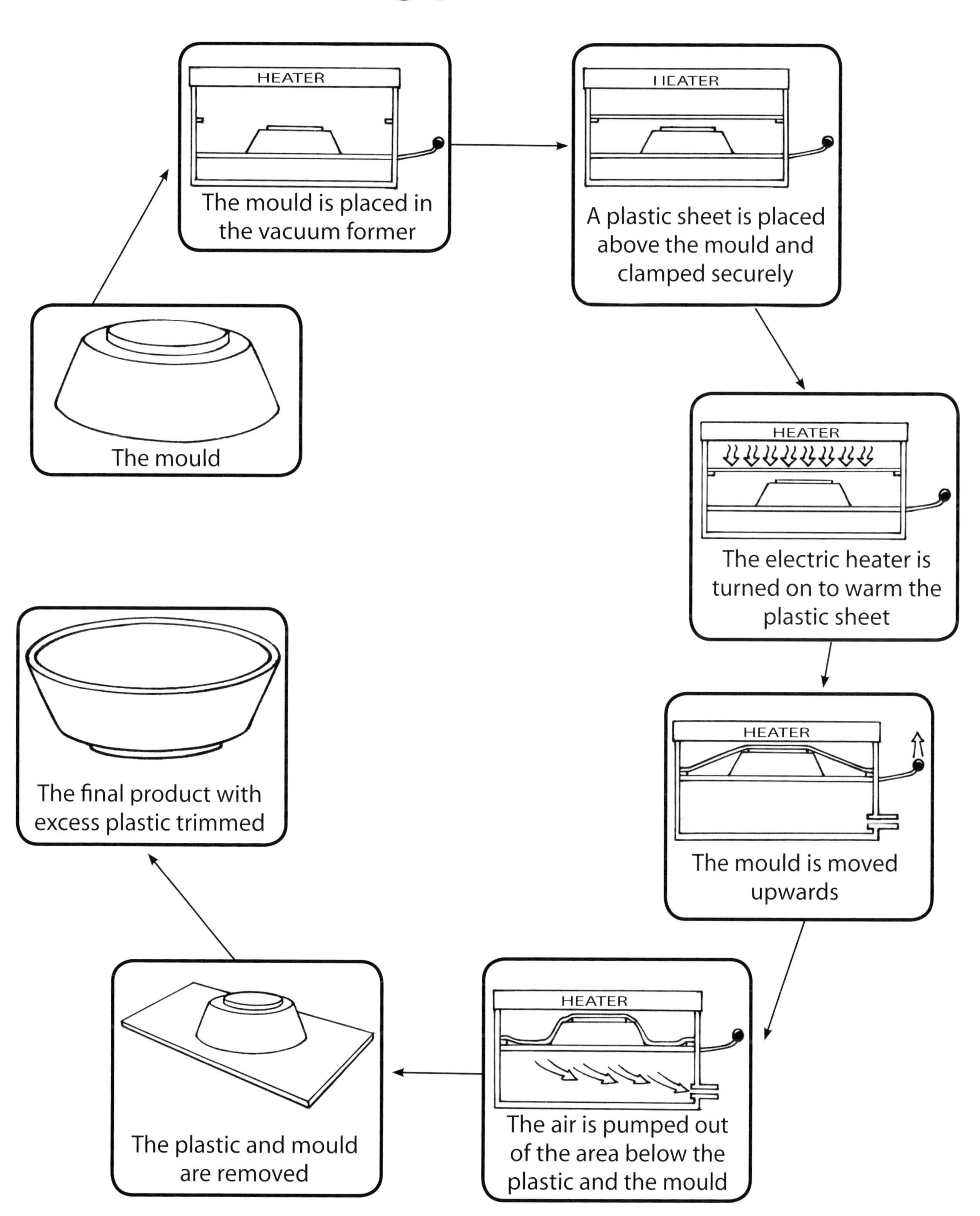

One-off and batch production (1)

During this activity, you are going to try to find out if it is quicker to make single items or batches of products. Your teacher will give you a kit for a product that you are going to make. It may be similar to the Lego® product shown below.

☞ For your first task you need to each build one of the products above on your own. Time how long it takes you to build one.

Sketch of your product:

☞ It took ______ seconds to build one product.

- How could you build them more quickly?
- If you worked as a group, how would you build as many products as possible in a given time?

One-off and batch production (2)

☞ As you will be working in a group, you will each need specific roles, for example, 'chassis builder' or 'final assembler'. In your groups, assign yourselves individual roles. Then write these jobs and who will be doing them in the table below.

	Job	Name
Role 1		
Role 2		
Role 3		
Role 4		
Role 5		

☞ Carry out the task to build as many products as possible in the time given.

How many did you make? ____________________

What were the advantages of making a product in this way?

____

____

If you were to do this task differently, what would you do?

____

____

____

How did you check the quality of the product? Was that someone's job?

____

Using jigs

To help us make small numbers of identical components or products in the Design and technology workshop, we can use jigs.

A jig can be used to help mark, cut or bend material and drill holes accurately.

☞ The picture below shows a jig that has been used to bend a piece of plastic accurately. Something is missing that could make it more accurate. What do you think it is? Place your answer in the box marked **a**) below.

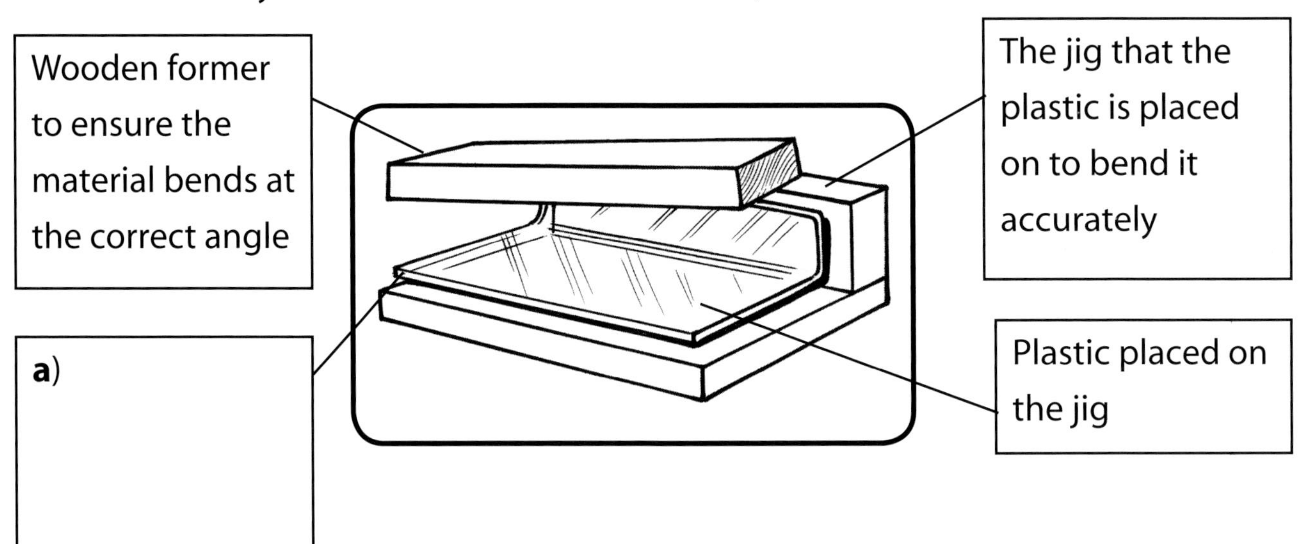

☞ In the box below, design a jig to help you in your own project. Use the one above as a guide. Label it to show how it works and explain what you are using the jig for.

Matching products to processes

☞ Match the products in the left-hand column to the methods of production in the right-hand column. One has been done for you.

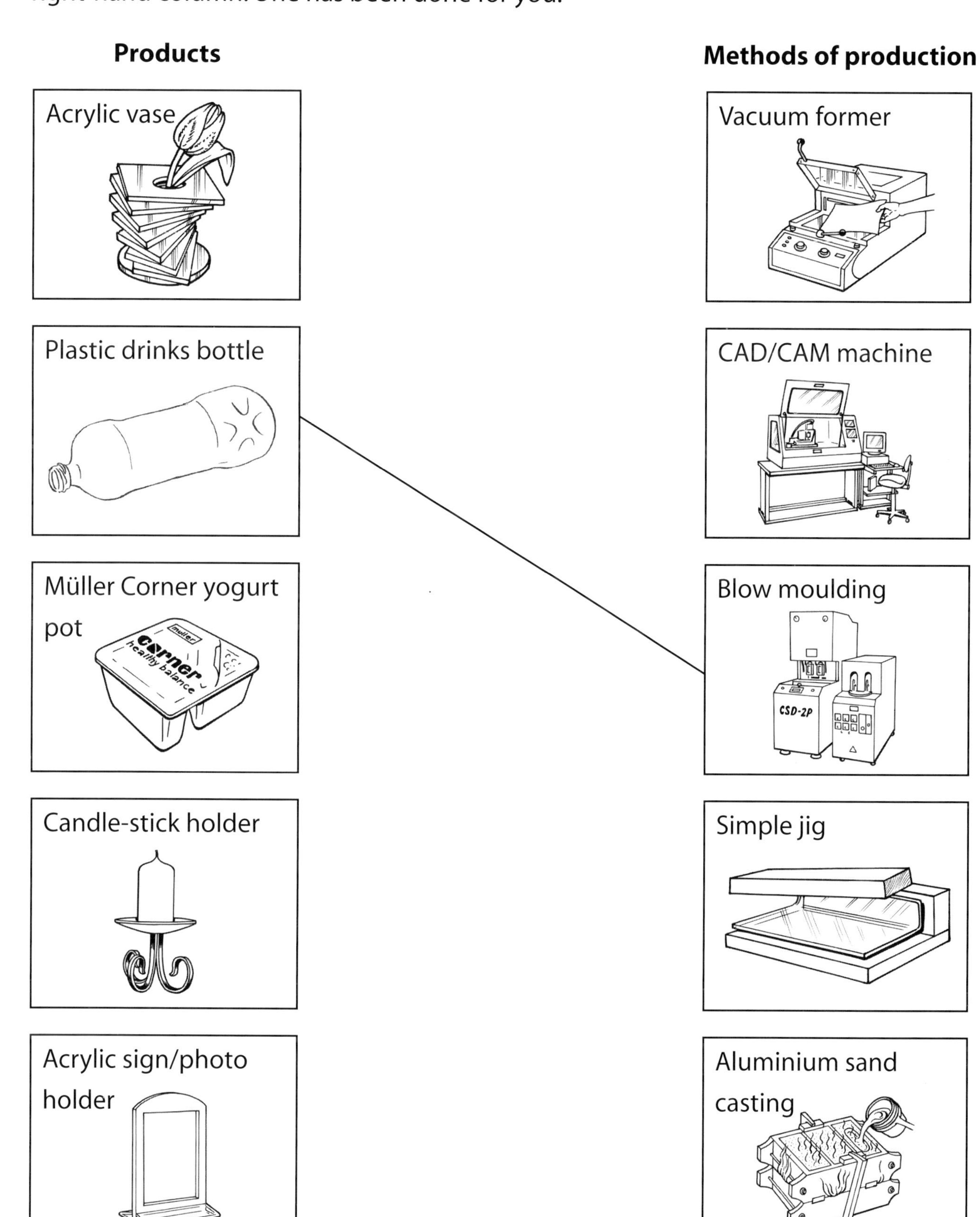

Teacher's notes

Computer-Aided Design and Manufacture

Objectives

- To be able to recognise and name the common elements of a CAD/CAM system
- To know that CAD/CAM can produce batches of the same product
- To explore the terms 'handmade' and 'mass produced' and their impact

Prior knowledge

To achieve these objectives, students should be able to use a PC with a mouse to enable them to use suitable graphics packages.

QCA links

Unit 8c Using ICT to support making.

NC links

2) Working with tools, equipment, materials and components to produce quality products: (a).

Northern Ireland PoS

Knowledge and understanding – manufacturing materials, components, techniques and processes.

Scottish attainment targets

Environmental Studies – Technology
Strand – Needs and how they are met
Level E
Strand – Processes and how they are applied
Level D
Environmental Studies – Skills in Technology – designing and making
Strand – Carrying out tasks
Level E

Welsh PoS

Designing skills: 7) and Making skills: 6).

Background

As design and manufacturing in industry is becoming more and more automated with the onset and development of Computer-Aided Design and Manufacture, it is important that students are able to understand and use the process within the Design and Technology classroom. Other considerations that students should be aware of are the impact that this has on originality and that there is a growing demand for bespoke products in the marketplace.

Starter activity

Start by asking students what they understand by the terms 'Computer-Aided Design' and 'Computer-Aided Manufacture'. Come up with a class-agreed definition for each. Ask students to list the components that make up a CAD/CAM system. Can they identify any of those items in the room?

Resource and activity sheets

Hand out a copy of 'An example of Computer-Aided Design and Manufacture' to all students and ask them to discuss it. Talk through the process shown: a step-by-step process of producing a product by CAD/CAM.

Use 'The CAD/CAM process' to introduce the students to the CAD/CAM facilities you have in your workshop. Ask them to make a quick sketch of the machines and name them. Ask the students to use the remainder of the sheet to produce a sketch of the design they are going to make using the CAD/CAM process. Once the students are familiar with the process and have possibly made a product using CAD/CAM, ask them to complete 'Using CAD/CAM' to explain the stages in the process.

'Advantages and disadvantages of CAD/CAM' starts to explore the benefits and drawbacks of CAD/CAM. To introduce this sheet, discuss the impact of CAD/CAM technologies on society. It may be best to do this by posing a number of questions for different groups to respond to, before asking students to complete the sheet. Once students have completed the sheet go through it as a class.

To reinforce this discussion, ask students to complete 'Methods of manufacture' to identify products made through CAD/CAM and those made by hand, and then to justify their decisions.

Plenary

Give groups cards with different key words on relating to this unit and ask them to explain what they mean to the rest of the class. Give the groups two or three minutes to come up with the explanation before they have to deliver it.

An example of Computer-Aided Design and Manufacture

☞ Here is an example of the CAD/CAM process that might be used in schools:

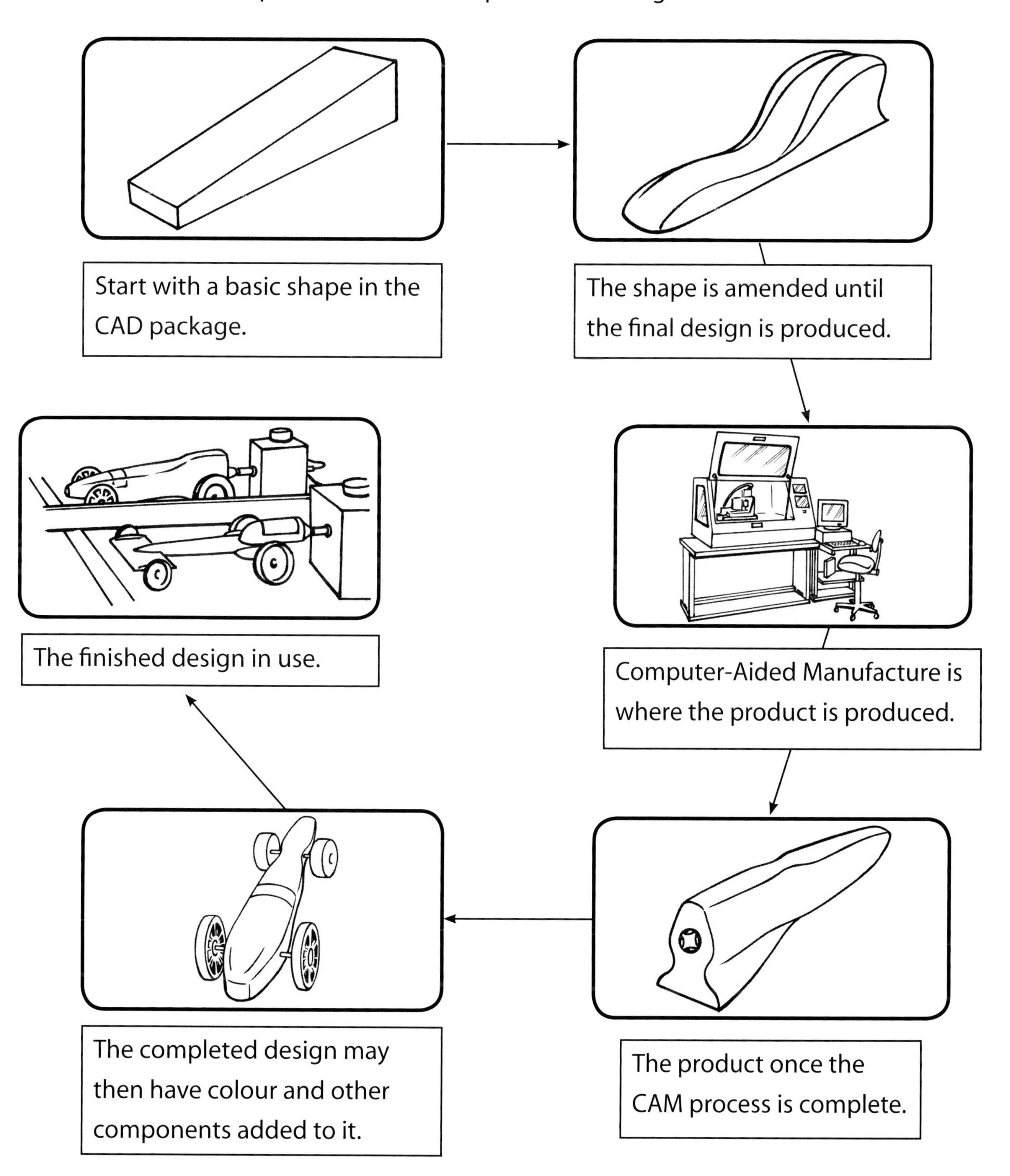

The CAD/CAM process

- CAD stands for Computer-Aided Design.
- CAM stands for Computer-Aided Manufacture.

CAD/CAM enables you to design your product on a computer, CAD, and then manufacture it on a machine attached to the computer, CAM.

☞ Have a look around your room and see if you can find any CAD/CAM equipment. Make a quick sketch of what you can see in the boxes below and label each one.

Name:______________	**Name:**______________	**Name:**______________

☞ Make a quick sketch of what you are going to design and make using the CAD/CAM equipment in this project.

Using CAD/CAM

☞ Use this page to make sketches and notes about how you have used CAD/CAM to make a product in your Design and Technology lessons. Use the word bank below to help you.

Stage 1

Stage 2

Stage 3

Stage 4

Stage 5

Word bank

designed	computer	finished	acrylic	router
CAD	CAM	connected	machined	

☞ In your workbook, describe your finished product. What have you had to do since it was produced by CAD/CAM?

Advantages and disadvantages of CAD/CAM

☞ Manufacturing products using machines has a number of advantages over producing products by hand. Can you think of three?

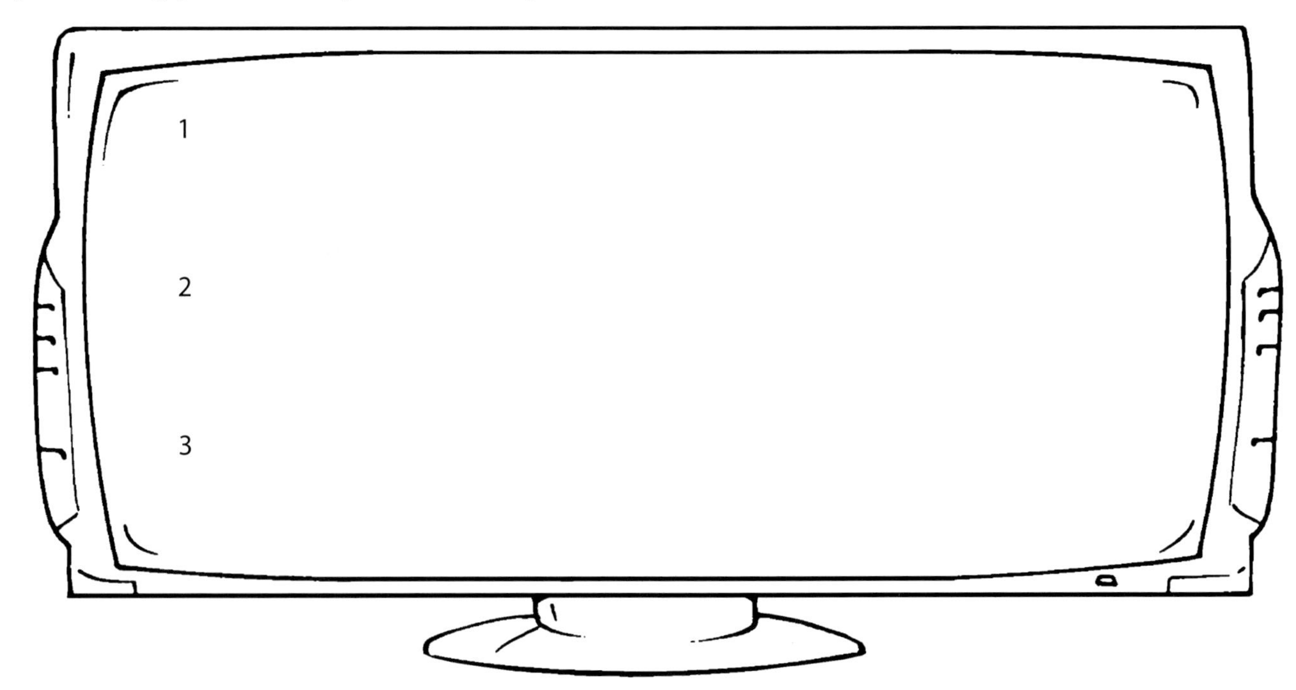

☞ While there are lots of benefits of making things with machines, there are also disadvantages. Can you think of three?

☞ In conclusion, which production method do you think is better? Explain your answer in your workbook.

Methods of manufacture

☞ Do you think the objects in the table below have been manufactured by hand or using CAD/CAM? Complete the table, explaining the reasons for your choices.

Product	Produced by	Reasons
Acrylic vase		
Gold ring		
Acrylic maze		
Jewellery box		
Desk		
Coffee table		

Teacher's notes

Product evaluation

Objectives

- To be able to evaluate their own work and work produced by others
- To understand the importance of carrying out quality checks during the making process
- To be able to produce a quality control checklist for a product they are making

Prior knowledge

Students should be able to link the main concepts in this unit to those that were examined in 'Designing with resistant materials'. They should be able to recognise the need to evaluate a finished product against the needs of a user.

QCA links

Unit 8b (ii) Designing for clients – resistant materials.

NC links

3) Evaluating processes and products: (b).

Northern Ireland PoS

Designing h).

Scottish attainment targets

Environmental Studies – Technology
Strand – Needs and how they are met
Level D
Environmental Studies – Skills in Technology – designing and making
Strand – reviewing and reporting on tasks
Levels D and E

Welsh PoS

Designing skills: 8) and Making skills: 7).

Background

Once a student has completed a project, they should evaluate it against a specification. The evaluation determines if the product will meet all of the needs of the user. An evaluation should use the same criteria as the specification in order to help gauge the suitability of the designs. It is possible to do this during the design stage to help pick out the most suitable design.

Starter activity

Question students on what they think an evaluation is. Have a number of products on the students' desks and ask them why and when we should evaluate products. Give students time to discuss their answers in groups before asking each group a question.

Resource and activity sheets

Hand out the resource sheet 'Product evaluation' and go through it with students, outlining in practice how evaluation is used.

Introduce 'Evaluating products' and ask students to discuss in pairs why we evaluate products and to list as many important reasons as they can think of. Pick students at random to share one of their reasons with the rest of the class. For the second part of the sheet, ask students to look at the products and come up with a list of tests they would carry out to see if each product is suitable. Ask the students why knowing the target group is important when deciding what tests to carry out.

'Quality control' examines a quality control process that could be used during the making of a simple product. Go through this with the students before asking them to come up with their own quality control process for making a CD storage system. As an extension, you could ask students to produce this as a group and then present their system to the whole class.

Introduce 'Designing quality control processes' to the group and then ask them to design a quality control process for a product that they are making. This will build upon the knowledge and understanding that they have gained so far.

'Evaluating the finished product' uses CAFE QUE (cost, aesthetics, function, ergonomics, quality, user, environment) as a framework to help students evaluate their products. Students should complete this individually and include a comment to explain their scoring. The box at the bottom of the sheet encourages the students to reflect on how they could improve their product.

Plenary

Place the students into small groups and give each of them a product. Ask them to evaluate it and then present their findings to another group, who should ask questions based on the evaluation given. Question groups on the process and purpose of evaluation to reinforce the concepts being used.

Product evaluation

Are all products as good or well made as each other?

☞ The products below show some faults that have occured but should have been picked up during product evaluation or testing. See how other products can overcome these problems.

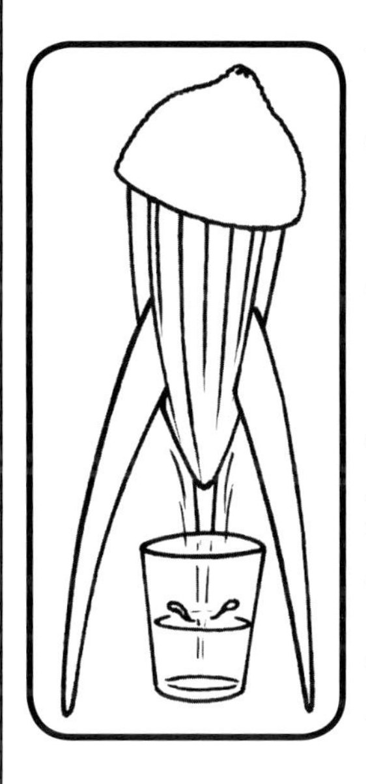

The lemon squeezer on the left is really nice to look at and display in a house. However, it is quite awkward to use as you need to find a glass to fit under it and there is nothing to catch the pips.

This lemon squeezer overcomes the problem of catching the pips with the strainer but it could be quite difficult to pour the juice out without making a mess.

This watering can looks comfortable to carry and use with the handle design but it could be awkward to fill and difficult to see when the water gets close to the top.

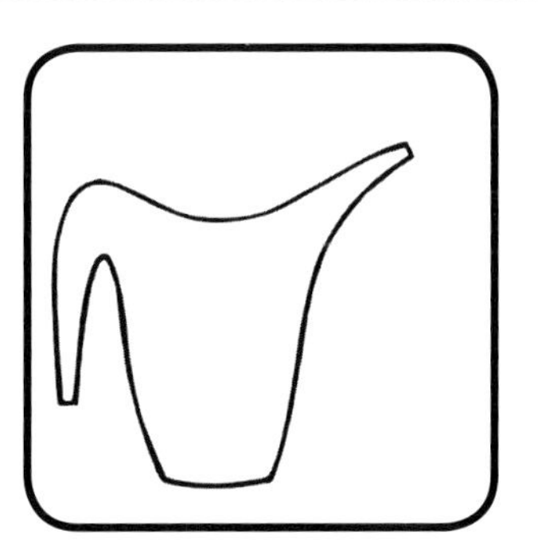

The watering can above looks stylish but is it as functional? It could be difficult to carry when full, and where is the full point? Is the water going to flow out by the handle or over the side if it is overfilled?

Evaluating products

☞ In pairs, discuss: Why do we test products? List as many reasons as you can.

☞ For the two products below, list the checks you would carry out.

Wooden train for children over the age of three

Wooden bookcase for a teenager's bedroom

Quality control

☞ The diagram below is a flow chart that shows the quality checks that would be carried out to make the simple jewellery box shown.

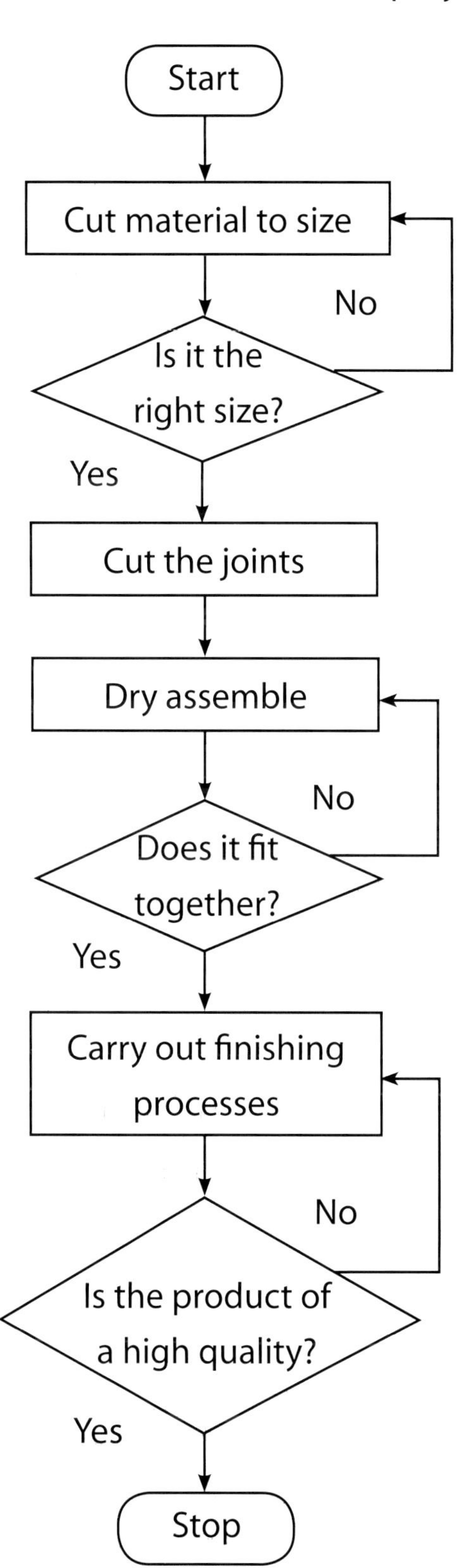

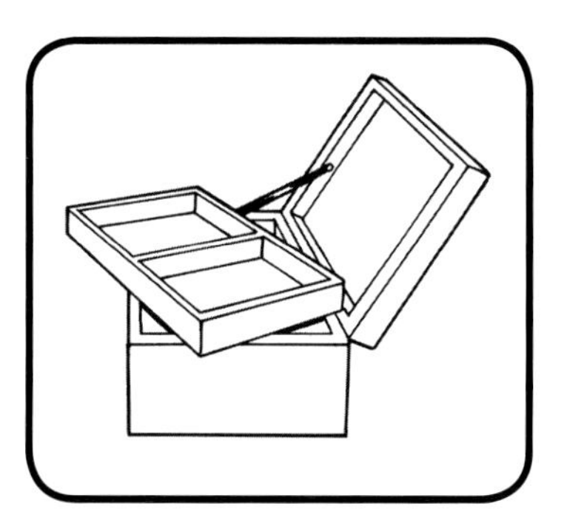

☞ Draw your own quality control chart for a CD storage unit using the flow chart opposite. What other checks would you make?

Designing quality control processes

☞ Use this page to design a quality control process for a project you are making. Remember to list the checks you will carry out during the making process, as well as those once the product is completed.

I am making a ________________________________.

Use the box on the left to draw a quick sketch of what you are making.

My quality control process:

Evaluating the finished product

Once you are happy with a product you have made, it is important to evaluate it against your design brief.

☞ Use the framework below to evaluate the product you have made.

Place a photograph of your finished product in this box.

When choosing the score, remember:

1 = Does not meet the criteria

2 = Okay, mostly meets the criteria

3 = Good, fully meets and possibly exceeds the criteria

Criteria	1	2	3	Comment
Cost				
Aesthetics (how it looks)				
Function (what it does)				
Ergonomics (comfort in use)				
Quality (materials and finish)				
User				
Environment (where it will be used)				

Overall comment – How could it be improved?

Assessment sheet – Resistant materials

Tick the boxes to show what you know or what you can do.

	know / yes	not sure / sometimes	don't know / no
1 I listen to the teacher			
2 I can work well with a partner			
3 I can work well in a group			
4			
5			
6			
7			
8			
9			
10			

I know best / I can do best:

....

....

....

I need to: (write no more than three targets)

....

....

....